the world within
women

To Kate

Long Live the programme

Thankyou for your dedication
and enthusiasm

with love .
Jane Carmenell

the world within
women

*the femenome guide to your
menstrual cycle*

. . . a remembering

Jane Catherine Severn

Published 2021
by Luna House Books
www.lunahouse.co.nz

A catalogue record for this book is available from the National Library of New Zealand

ISBN 978-0-473-56849-8 (Softcover)
ISBN 978-0-473-56850-4 (Epub)
ISBN 978-0-473-56851-1 (Kindle)

Printed by The Copy Press, Nelson, New Zealand.
www.copypress.co.nz

Moonflowers

Do you know about moonflowers? If you go looking for them by the ordinary light of day you will never find them. To learn their astonishing secrets, you have to adjust your eyes to their world. Only in darkness will these luminous and fragrant beauties reveal themselves to you. Only if you really want to know them. Only if you are willing to view things in a very different light…

Contents

My proofs derive from experience and my own reasoning, and not from reference to authorities… It is not title and eloquence, nor the knowledge of languages, nor the reading of many books … that are the requirements of a physician, but the deepest knowledge of things themselves and of nature's secrets, and this knowledge outweighs all else…

Paracelsus, announcing his lectures in 1526[1]

---

1   Jolande Jacobi (ed) and Norbert Guterman (Tr), *Paracelsus, Selected Writings*, Second Edition, Revised, Bollingen Foundation Inc, New York, 1958. Published by Pantheon Books Inc, NY, p liii

Introduction

My dear women

Within you shines a replica of the universe. Just as a tiny seed contains a great tree, so each girl and woman who has ever lived has carried inside her the imprint of the whole cosmos. In more ways than we have ever been told, our intimate and intricate feminine design repeats and resonates with all of the fourfold rhythms and patterns in Nature – the impulses that create and sustain life itself. Through its hormonally initiated sequence of changes, this elegant and eloquent guidance system is active and speaking to us from within every day of our life. And yet few of us realise it is there, for we have long been conditioned to live as if it were not.

Over a full lifetime we all traverse the four stages of a uniquely feminine metacycle: firstly menarche, our entry into womanhood, which we recognise by our first period; then the many years of our menstrual cycles (each containing its own four phases); next, the great transition of menopause; and lastly the crowning stage of mature life. What we have generally been taught is that the onset of menstruation marks the beginning of our reproductive capacity, and its ending at menopause signals our loss of that fertility. While this is of course true, there is much, much more for us to realise about ourselves and the potent and beautiful lives our female hormones equip us to live.

Here on Planet Earth, Nature is a mirror into which we can look to see ourselves reflected – to discover what we are made of, how we make sense, and all the bigger pictures we are part of. There is nothing in this book that you do not already know, for the story upon these pages has always been written in your body and sung throughout the cosmos.

And yet you may not know that you know. This knowledge may feel new, yet strangely familiar and obvious to you. You may never have encountered it before, and yet wonder how you could have been unaware of these simple, self-evident truths about your own daily experience.

Sadly, throughout many of the cultures of our world, knowledge of menarche, menstrual cycles, menopause and mature life has been obscured, and a veil cast over the mirrors in Nature that would reflect our own perfection to us. That veil is made of ignorance, born of fear and prejudice. For a long, long time – indeed since patriarchy assumed dominance some 5000 years ago – we humans have been distracted by our efforts to separate ourselves from Nature and to conquer it. We have forgotten the arts of living by our true design and tried to impose artificial 'improvements' upon ourselves. These have caused such alienation and suffering that we no longer trust or even recognise the voices of our femininity speaking within us. A strange silence has fallen into the world, a vacuum of collective amnesia. Lulled by its longevity, we fail to notice we do not even have a name by which we can call our intrinsic female design.

The void of namelessness has kept us quiet, and worse, ignorant, about who we are for far too long. How can we speak of, or understand in ourselves, something for which we have no language? We have the dots, but we do not connect them. We have the evidence, but we've been taught to despise it. It is our metacycle, unnamed but powerfully present, that imprints the particular and purposeful design of the feminine into every woman's body and psyche, awaiting our awakening to its vast potentials.

The absence of a name presents us with a conundrum: how can we know what we can't yet name? But then how can we name what we don't yet know? Perhaps, though, just as it is the blinding night that beguiles a moonflower into unfurling her petals and revealing her exquisite face, so too this oddly dark space in our consciousness may offer us a rich and precious opportunity, a tabula rasa or blank slate upon which we ourselves can write in newly visible ink.

As I embarked many years ago on my quest of gathering the fragments of our lost knowledge and carefully reassembling them, I created as a temporary measure the

the world within women

term **menstruality** so we could begin to speak of our **four-m sequence** of menarche, menstrual cycle years, menopause and mature life with a single word, and to understand it as a single entity. The name menstruality describes the actual workings of our feminine design: ovulation, periods, pre-menstrual feelings, mood and energy changes around the month, hot flushes, mental and memory changes, intensified emotions, aging processes – all the many and varied experiences our hormonal changes bring to us at every stage. **Conscious menstruality** is the practical application of menstruality knowledge in our daily lives – the simple and sacred art of living by our own nature with awareness, trust, ease and enjoyment.

These new words have served well for a number of years to get us started on our quest of breaking the silence. But they have only been able to take us part of the way. It is time to go further now. We have long been listening for the true name of our menstruality, the source of all its mysteries, the maker of the matrix that shapes our womanhood. A name is a key that can open a realm of knowledge. It is an energetic signature, or imprint. A name is a declaration, announcing an existence, making its presence felt, seen, heard, real, usable and ordinary. The right word carries the essence, the feeling of what it names. Naming our four-m sequence is like holding up a mirror so that what has been latent inside us will recognise itself and burst vibrantly back into life once again.

I have served a long apprenticeship in the study of menstruality – just long enough at 37 years to know I am still at the beginning; that what I have glimpsed has so much more to reveal to us yet. For many of those years I could not hear the name I was listening for, much as I wanted to. I knew, of course, that the naming was not mine to create. That the task of a quest is to be willing to live its quest-ion, humbly and patiently, for long enough that the answer appears of its own accord. To wait until it becomes so self-evident that we wonder why we could not hear it before.

Then one morning as I lay in my bed in the drifty space between sleeping and waking, I saw behind my still-closed eyes a cottage garden, rampant with many kinds of flowers. And there amongst them, lying on the soil, was a word. Bending over it to look more closely I saw it was the word I had so long been expecting, a single word holding a universe in many parts.

The purpose of this book and its following volumes is to bring a new sound into the world – the sound of women speaking in a whole new way about what has been unmentionable. That sound is the name *femenome.*

> We have a new name for the un-named feminine metacycle: menarche/ menstrual cycle years/menopause/mature life. It is called **the femenome**

Just as the whole map of a species' genes is called its *genome,* so we can now use the word *femenome* to describe our inherent feminine design. The femenome is the complete lexicon of spiritual and energetic information for being female that is stored in every woman's hormonal circuitry. It is the garden in which we grow our Self, the matrix, or motherboard, governing our lifelong psycho-spiritual maturation.

The femenome is an energetic entity, the omni-presence (everywhere present) of the divine feminine aspect of life itself. And it is at the same time our own individual and personal expression of that entity, that nature, within our female human body. We are the stars in her galaxy, the numberless leaves in her forests, all made of her yet no two alike. She is ours. We are hers. She has been banished into dormancy for longer than human memory can stretch. And now she is awakening.

This is a very small book about a very big subject – a brief introduction to just one stage in a four-stage process that is designed to be learned and absorbed over a whole lifetime. The femenome is as deep as the ocean, as vast as the cosmos. It is truly boundless in scope, for it is all about consciousness. There are no limits to that. My hope is that this brief overview will give you a new window to look through; new language to speak and understand, and some tools and navigational aids to help you work with your own menstrual cycle experience. It will reveal to you a journey that is no less than sublime. Take your time. A journey (from the French word *jour,* for day) is something undertaken day-by-day. You do not have to be clever to learn this knowledge, and you don't have to go anywhere to find it. You just need to remember to do one simple, but utterly life-changing and long-forbidden thing: to *trust* the inherent femaleness inside you on its own terms. The destination is your fully realised Self, your divine nature, and the path to reach that is mapped out for you to follow every day by the hormonal template of your four-m feminine life sequence. You don't need to call her – she will call you!

Please note that the model and processes offered in this book will not exactly fit any woman's individual experience. They are in no way intended as something you should try to fit yourself into. The femenome (being feminine) can never be standardised, predictable or contained into a definitive version. It is infinitely variable. Your cycle, your menstruality experience, will be different from any other woman's, and what is more, each one of your cycles will be different from any other you have had. I present this model in the hope that it will inspire and encourage you to create your own personal and flexible version, to recognise the rhythms, patterns and changes that are unique to you, month by month.

Does this book contain new knowledge? No. What is written here has always existed because it is simply the nature of things and the things of nature. But neither will this book suggest we should go back to old ways or traditions. Like the season of spring, old as the planet but new, invigorating and refreshing every year, this knowledge is an eternal truth, waiting to be brought to light when we have most keenly been feeling its absence.

Now, as we recognise the darkness of our unawareness, the soft luminosity of the moonflower begins to unfurl. Its time has come.

Acknowledgements

The knowledge I am sharing with you in this book has come to me in ways I never could have planned or known in advance – ways that will leave me forever humbled, grateful and delighted.

I acknowledge with utmost love this work's primary source, the femenome herself, present in every woman on Earth and in all the patterns, rhythms and energies of Nature around us. What I offer you here has largely been learned directly from her, through my own experience and my observations of her workings in countless women around me. My beloved professional roles as psychotherapist and Pascha therapist for women have privileged me with intimate insights into their lives over several decades now, and taught me more than I could ever measure.

Through my years of workshops, courses, seminars and celebrations at Luna House I have shared the quest of re-discerning our original design with so many wonderful women. To all of you who have been my teachers by being my students I send my utmost gratitude. Thank you for your warm and enthusiastic receptivity to conscious menstruality, and for showing me in your lives the difference it makes. You are the ones who are giving the knowledge of the femenome a strong and grounded foundation in the real world of the 21st century, and passing it on to those in whom it will truly flower – the beautiful girls of humanity's next generation.

Much of what this book contains has been accessed through my sleep state, in meditation, or purely intuitively. It is well beyond the power of words to describe my

the world within women

gratitude for the teachings of Raman Pascha and Yasmeen Clark[2] through whom I have learned to trust these sources of knowing unquestioningly. Without their love, support, guidance and tuition over the years, I may not have been able to maintain my confidence and conviction in presenting a viewpoint that differs so greatly from the socially-sanctioned science of our times.

Yasmeen Clark is also the creator and teacher of Pascha Therapy. Her training of me as a therapist and teacher in this modality has been both foundational and formative in my development of conscious menstruality, particularly in its way of responding to the feelings and emotions women encounter in their cycles. Her contribution to my life, and this work, is inestimable. If this book and the others to come in the series can acknowledge and honour Yasmeen's work as well as my own, that will be a small gesture toward my unrepayable debt for her vast but unseen part in it.

We are witnessing throughout the world these days a most heartening array of books, websites, blogs, workshops and courses, rituals and celebrations of the feminine. Awareness and restoration of our long-lost menstruality is building and swelling in delicious and exciting ways, gathering speed and volume like the great wave of consciousness it is, sweeping back across the thirsty world. To every single writer, healer, facilitator and teacher in this ever-growing mosaic of redemption, I offer my warmest thanks and admiration. May your work come to a fruition sweeter than you can dream of as you do it.

There are writers I wish to acknowledge and thank specifically for their particular and significant contributions to my own years of searching out menstruality's secrets. Penelope Shuttle and Peter Redgrove first woke me up to the meaning of menstruation, and to the whole menstrual cycle, with their astoundingly rich and ground-breaking book, *The Wise Wound: Menstruation and Everywoman*[3]. Their extensive and scholarly work was the catalyst for me, and radically altered the direction of my life, both personally and professionally.

---

2   Raman Pascha (The Master Khamouri) is a spiritual master channelled through his beloved Yasmeen since 1986. Through their centre, Pascha Nourishing Body and Soul, they offer public talks, courses, meditations and workshops, as well as personal consultations. Yasmeen has created a new feelings-based and soul-centred therapy called Pascha Therapy, for which a three year training course is offered at the centre in Christchurch, New Zealand. See www.pascha.co.nz for further information.

3   Penelope Shuttle and Peter Redgrove, *The Wise Wound: Menstruation and Everywoman* [Revised Edition], Paladin, Grafton Books, London, 1986

I am also deeply indebted to Miranda Gray[4] for her mandala presentation of the menstrual cycle, from which I drew my initial understanding of its four phases and energies. Reading *Red Moon: Understanding and Using the Gifts of the Menstrual Cycle* helped me to do exactly that. I acknowledge that my own model of menstruality rests upon the foundation of her pioneering work, and develops it further.

Lara Owen contributed very helpful historical and social context, as well as a most compassionate and practical gift with *Honouring Menstruation*[5], a book most worthy of its title, and Dena Taylor also deepened my understanding of menstruation with *Red Flower: Rethinking Menstruation*[6].

In a more academic vein, Riane Eisler's superb classic *The Chalice and the Blade*[7] sent wave after wave of goose bumps through me as I felt the enormity of historical context in which the return of menstruality consciousness is situated. Paula Weideger's extensive anthropological research is a treasury of history, context, and validation of what has survived under the surface of every woman's skin, and I thank her for *Female Cycles*, and *Menstruation and Menopause*[8]. Anne Walker, too, inspired me with her meticulous research and energetic critique in *The Menstrual Cycle*[9].

Anita Diamant's deservedly popular novel *The Red Tent*[10] is by far the most lent book in my Luna House library, spurring me on in the sure knowledge that women do hunger for books on menstruality, while Rosemary Menzies' heart-breaking *Poems for Bosnia* and *New Poems for Bosnia*[11] strengthened my resolve to do the one small thing I can to hasten the return of women's words, women's hearts, women's knowing to the body politic.

To friends and family who have stood by me, accommodated me, encouraged me, believed in me, even though at times understandably questioning why anyone would put

---

4   Miranda Gray, *Red Moon: Understanding and Using the Gifts of the Menstrual Cycle*, Element Books, England, 1994
5   Lara Owen, *Honouring Menstruation*, The Crossing Press, California, 1998
6   Dena Taylor, *Red Flower: Rethinking Menstruation*, The Crossing press, California, 1988
7   Riane Eisler, *The Chalice and the Blade: Our History, Our Future*, HarperCollins, New York, 1988
8   Paula Weideger, *Female Cycles*, The Women's Press, London, 1978 and *Menstruation and Menopause*, Dell, New York, 1977 (revised and expanded edition)
9   Anne Walker, *The Menstrual Cycle*, Routledge, London, 1997
10 Anita Diamant, *The Red Tent*, Picador, New York, 1997
11 Rosemary Menzies, *Poems for Bosnia* and *New Poems for Bosnia*, Illyria Press, Auckland NZ, 1994, 1998

herself through so much for so long in the cause of such a deeply unpopular and financially destitute subject as menstruality, my undying love and thanks. You will probably never know how much your patience and generosity have helped. Through all the years and decades of my preoccupation, my many despairs, you did not disappear. I owe my perseverance, and the final birthing after this long, long labour, to you all.

An Invitation

As you make your way through this book you will come across reflections and exercises that I hope will help to make its knowledge relevant and useful for you in personal and practical ways. You may like to find yourself a very special journal book or folder, and pens and pencils, paints or pastels to accompany your reading. I would suggest you choose blank rather than lined pages, and good quality paper, so you can draw as well as write.

Exercises in conscious menstruality cannot be done from our mind. You might enjoy creating a very feminine ambience for yourself as you come to the personal reflections. Light a candle; choose a fragrance; play music you love; wrap yourself in your favourite colour… slow your breathing and turn to the place inside you where your deepest wishes for yourself reside. Listen for the answers and inspirations that come from that source. They will be different from those that we know as 'normal'. And because of that, they will be answers and inspirations that can truly change your life and our world. Believe them.

If you already know how to track your cycle, do make this an everyday practice now, using your journal or a calendar, and recording your observations of how your energy, mood, thoughts and feelings flow and fluctuate around your month. If you are not yet familiar with doing this, you will find detailed guidance and suggestions a little further along in this book.

You may also like to do the exercises and meditations offered here with a friend, or in a group of women who meet regularly. Our menstrual cycle is designed to be lived communally rather than individually, and you will find that sharing your experiences of these reflections with other women will help immensely in coming to know the femenome in all its rich variety and depth of detail.

X

A note for women whose menstrual cycle is irregular, prevented or affected by medical issues, hormonal contraception or any other factors

Very sadly in our times women's sensitive hormonal design is subjected to a multitude of pressures from chemical pollutants and practices, from the stresses of a lifestyle that does not allow for menstruality, from ever-escalating sources of radiation, from medication and from epidemical levels of illnesses whose real causes have yet to be properly investigated. Any or all of these things can disrupt or even disallow our experience of our cycles as they are naturally designed to occur.

It is most important to understand that the femenome belongs to **all** women throughout their lives, regardless of physical or medical circumstances. Because our understanding of the four m's (menarche, menstrual cycles, menopause, mature life) has become limited to the physical, reproductive function, women who no longer menstruate (or have never menstruated) as a result of medical conditions or surgical interventions are often left to feel that they have lost their cycle, or their whole natural menstruality. This, understandably, can seem major and permanent, a grief that can leave women feeling deprived of a deep and precious part of themselves.

If your menstrual life has been disrupted by hysterectomy, chemotherapy, endometriosis, polycystic ovary, or other procedures, medications or conditions, it is vitally important that you understand you cannot lose your *menstruality*. Even if you have lost your ovaries or their function, your years of living in your menstrual cycle will mean its cadences are imprinted on your psyche. If you do not have periods to alert you to your cyclical process, the femenome will still be present in your womanly nature, your changing energies and your states of consciousness.

The visible and tangible experiences of menstrual cycles and menopause are physical signs of internal processes that go much deeper in us than just the physiological. They are like guides or teachers by which women learn their special feminine nature. When the outward, visible signs can no longer occur, the invitation is for women to learn their attunement to the femenome through other voices. If you are a woman who has chosen or reassigned for herself an identification with the feminine, this book is also for you. There are many ways in which we can track our cycles and keep in touch with the energetic and spiritual tides that rise and fall inside us as the months and years of our lives proceed. What follows is designed to help you do this through a deep awareness of the femenome's design, and by alerting you to the many ways in which its purposeful changes are echoed and supported by Nature's rhythms and cycles. For you especially, the moon will be a faithful ally to assist your re-attunement to yourself.

Similarly, women who have chosen (or been offered no alternative to) hormonal or ovulation-suppressing contraceptive methods will find the voice of their femenome muffled, as if listening to music from under water. The knowledge contained in these pages is for and about you in a very particular way, for in truth no woman in these times is given her right to make a **fully informed** choice. Contraception is such a vital issue in women's lives, deserving of the best possible support. Sadly, those who, with the very best of intentions, advocate and administer birth control or pain relief remedies that disrupt women's natural cycles, simply do not know what it is they are so expediently eliminating.

Every woman, regardless of her medical history, deserves to know that she can embody and cherish her menstruality as her own personal and inalienable possession. It is this book's express intention to celebrate the femenome in all women, and to extend a special, inclusive welcome to those who have experienced the loss or absence of its outward signs. I hope you will find in these pages much to encourage you to reclaim what is yours – your own deep feminine nature, and the developmental journey of your menstruality. Awareness is the key. By knowing the femenome energies we can learn to recognise, trust and creatively use them in our lives, even without the physical reminders.

I wish you a deeply joyous and satisfying femenome journey.

Finding the femenome – my story

As a young woman I detested my periods. Like many of my era, I had been supplied with only the scantiest of biological information, and a religious indoctrination on the innate inferiority and sinfulness of my gender. I could not escape the notion that menstruation was my inheritance of punishment as a daughter of Eve, the life-sentence I deserved for the 'original sin' of being born female. Every period increased my shame and self-loathing, and my depression at being unable to avoid this tell-tale stigma – the hideous secret that might shout its presence aloud at any moment if I relaxed my vigilance. By the age of twelve I was convinced that it was every woman's duty to resign herself to a secret blight of suffering about which she must never speak, let alone complain.

Then one day in my mid-twenties came a seemingly ordinary moment that has made more difference to my life than any other, before or since. In a book I would never have noticed[12] had a friend not asked me to hold it briefly, I read on a randomly opened page one sentence that changed, utterly and forever, my sense of what it is to be woman. Like the kiss of Sleeping Beauty's prince, its startling words awakened me from the sleep that does not know it is asleep.

I had never heard the simple fact that women's monthly cycles match those of the moon. That one piece of knowledge leapt up from the page and spun my world around until I could see everything in a bright new light. From that moment on I knew without doubt that

---

12 That book, that marvel of redemption, was *The Wise Wound: Menstruation and Everywoman* [Revised Edition, Paladin, Grafton Books, London, 1986] and to its authors, Penelope Shuttle and Peter Redgrove, I send a warm and joyous gratitude.

in the big realms beyond human culture women are a perfect fit! That we belong! That we make sense in ways we have never been told. I felt my life receive a sweet welcome home to a world in which I need no longer experience myself as an awkward misfit, hiding parts of my reality for fear of embarrassing myself or offending others. Simply by looking up into the sky I could be reassured that those parts of me that had felt most wrong, most out-of-step, most disgraceful, made the most sense of all. I was flooded with an ecstatic relief.

At that time I was travelling far from home, and the book had to be returned to my host's town library only moments later. But it had done its work. Inside me now was an excited certainty that there was more to find, more to know – knowledge we had never heard or dreamed of. As soon as I read that the moon is a mirror of women I realised that *every* day of our month has meaning, has a part to play – that a menstrual cycle is much more than just a period, and that women in their ordinary nature are marvellously multi-layered beings. I felt as if I had stumbled upon the corner of a buried treasure chest, sticking up through the sand. And I was right. My huge excitement and anticipation were sensing the presence of a body of knowledge so vast and so powerful that even one tiny fragment of it could change my life forever. I did not fully understand until later in my search that this was because the femenome is an immense and sacred holograph, a fractal – that all of it is contained, and can be discerned, in any part of it.

Though I could not have guessed it at the time, my momentary glance into that book had set me on a path that would become my life's work. Once the door had opened I could never close it again. That single precious glimmer of knowledge had cut into my world like the first shaft of bright light and colour through a clearing fog.

But like all revelations, it came with a double impact. Alongside my marvelling at the difference knowing made to me, and the instant disappearance of my premenstrual and menstrual miseries, came the shock of recognising the depth of women's dispossession in our times, and for hundreds of generations before us. Even a tiny amount of light can reveal something that is hidden in a dark place. But that light also shows how dark the darkness is. My one little spark of awareness showed me that the simplest and most necessary facts of our lives have been withheld from us, and we don't even know they are missing. Nowhere in our mainstream culture is the whole story of women's cyclical nature taught. Nowhere is it valued. Nor consulted. There is so much more to us than we realise, but deprived of our basic self-knowledge we are standing with our backs to the mirror, unable to see and unable to be who we really are.

How to set about restoring a loss of such magnitude? I instantly felt the vast and healing difference that could come into the world if its women were awake to themselves – contributing fully from their complex and variable femininity rather than striving to adapt to cultural norms that demand constancy. At first my determination to find the rest of the knowledge led me in futile and disappointing directions – I was yet to learn that the moonflower never reveals her face to those who hunt for her by the wrong light. Time and time again as I searched libraries, medical sources, early versions of the internet and even feminism, I found only limited and pathologised views of menstruality, and the eternal argument about whether women's notorious hormonal variability should or should not be allowed to affect their fitness for work and eligibility for positions of power and authority in society. In my eagerness to uncover deeper layers of the female psyche, I became a counsellor, and then a psychotherapist, specialising in women's issues. To my despair, though, these disciplines made no effort to see through or go beyond their medical origins, and seemed content to stay within traditional attitudes to each of the phases of the femenome.

As much as it frustrated me, my inability to find what I was looking for within accustomed sources of information gave me – or rather taught me – the vital key to a search of this nature. Having exhausted every other avenue, I had only one left to which I could turn: the femenome itself, as embodied and expressed in every woman's daily experience. To re-cognise (know differently) what the femenome really is we need only to be humble, willing and curious – prepared to accept its own terms, see it with unprejudiced eyes, pick up the cues of its long-forgotten language and re-tune ourselves to its abandoned frequencies. We need to dare to trust that taking the time to do so will open the way to a truly revolutionary adventure in our self-regard. Now in my fourth decade of immersion in study of the femenome it is taking me to places I never dreamed possible, pouring a seemingly limitless stream of revelations to confound my mind, expand my heart and beguile my soul.

What I have learned from this supreme teacher has become the simple (but not easy) approach, the revelatory re-search method that has created Luna House, my college of the femenome. Its steps of awareness and practice make up the pages of this handbook, and the others in the conscious menstruality series.

I thank you and all women for being my teachers by being female – for your courage and grace in bearing the unnamed mystery of the femenome in a world that does not recognise, acknowledge or support you for doing so. May your own discoveries of the ineffable beauty, sacredness and purpose of your menstruality bring you immense joy, and the company of millions of awakening women around the world in these changing times.

a pause to consider…

Take some time to reflect on your own initiation into awareness of menstrual cycles. You might like to write and draw some of your earliest experiences in your journal, or share them with friends or in your women's group. In this way you can gain a deeper understanding of how your first impressions shaped your later relationship with your menstruality. Be your most honest and compassionate self as you open the door of remembering how you began.

How did you first hear or learn about menstrual cycles? ~ How old were you when you first became aware of them? ~ When you got your first period? ~ What was conveyed to you, in obvious ways? ~ In subtle ways? ~ Did you gradually piece the information together, or did it all come in one download?

*What **knowledge** were you given? ~ By whom? ~ How was it presented? ~ What kind of **language** was used? ~ What **attitudes** did you absorb? ~ How did you feel you should respond to your own cycle when it came? ~ Did you have any worries about it? ~ Or did it excite you? ~ What did you feel you had to look forward to?*

What did you pick up from how menstrual cycles are presented in media? ~ In advertising? ~ What other sources of knowledge did you have?

Did you receive any instruction at school? ~ What was that like for you? ~ As a young girl, were you given an understanding of your cycle all around the month, or just menstruation? ~ What meanings did you sense in what was communicated from different sources?

What information was helpful? ~ What was not? ~ Was there enough? ~ Did it make sense to you? ~ How did it make you feel about being female? ~ About your future as a woman?

What words would most honestly describe your impressions? ~ What was your menarche (first period) experience like for you? ~ Do you remember that day clearly? ~ Or was it no big deal? ~ Were you prepared and waiting for it, or did it come as a surprise? ~ Was it as you expected, or different? ~ How did others around you respond to it? ~ Were you celebrated? ~ Or was it a private moment for you? ~ Did you receive the help and support you needed? ~ What would have made it easier or more meaningful for you?

How would you like to guide a beloved daughter toward and through her menarche?

PART ONE

Re-Cognising
the roots of our current experience

CHAPTER ONE

A little bit of history: how we learned not to know

Remember a time, perhaps 5000 years ago,[13] when entire populations of humanity lived in the sacred rhythms of woman-cycles. In those days there was no electric light to obliterate the waxing and waning of moonlight, and all women would ovulate together at the monthly stimulus of the full moon. And so they would then all menstruate together as well, at the dark of the moon fourteen days later. For the days of their bleeding, ordinary demands upon the women would cease. No longer were they expected to gather or cook food, take care of children, or maintain the usual routines. Instead they would retreat together to specially designated shelters to enter deeply and exclusively into their menstrual state of altered consciousness.

Far from seeing the feminine changes as disrupting the life of the community, these societies took the greatest of care not to disrupt the life of feminine cycles. Women's withdrawal to menstruate was held as a holy act, for this was known to be the time when they were sensitive, open to dreams, visions, insights and messages from the world of spirit. Instructions from the gods would be brought back to the village at the end of the menstrual period for the benefit of the whole tribe. The fourfold nature of the feminine lifecycle: menarche, menstrual cycle

---

13   Archaeologist Marija Gimbutas opened a radically new understanding of our past by uncovering a period of history she called Old European in which, until it was overwhelmed by more aggressive patriarchal cultures about 5000 years ago, populations lived in peaceful agricultural societies which were matrifocal, and goddess worshipping. She contends that there is no evidence for war, weapons or dominance of one gender by the other in these times, and that life was centred around the cycles of Nature. You can read about these times in any of her vast array of works, and also in Riane Eisler's *The Chalice and the Blade*, noted earlier. The above suggestion of how women's menstrual cycles were held in those cultures is made by many writers across a variety of genres and disciplines.

years, menopause and mature life, was recognised and celebrated as the perfect replica of Nature's seasonal cycles of spring, summer, autumn, winter – the menstrual cycle lived within the life cycle lived within the Nature cycle.

Remember how women's knowledge was valued, revered, sought after in those times. How it was seen as the essential complement to that which could be provided or accessed by men. How women trusted their affinity with life itself, and humankind lived in attunement to the sacred feminine.

Five millennia of patriarchal history have drastically changed humanity's relationship to the feminine. How has it come about that in our supposedly advanced 21st century civilisations so little is known about menstruality, and that what we do know is so often negatively expressed and painfully experienced? The story of how humanity's attitudes to our deep feminine nature have been deconstructed and reconstructed through the last five thousand years is a long and sorrowful one and far too big to be included in this small book[14]. And yet we need to know it exists, for in our own daily lives, even if we cannot identify it, we continue to feel the weight of this history bearing down on us.

We need to know enough of what shaped our cultural conditioning to make us able to catch its influences within ourselves. We cannot escape being infected by such a long history – but when we recognise where these assumptions come from we will much more easily be able to choose not to let them shape our own lives, and, most importantly, not to unconsciously pass them on to our daughters.

> We need to know how menstruality's history has constructed our own attitudes **because these familiar beliefs stop us from knowing what our menstruality actually is**

---

14   If you want to know more about the takeover of matriarchal consciousness by the masculine, there is no better source than Riane Eisler's brilliant account in *The Chalice and the Blade,* (*The Chalice and The Blade: Our History, Our Future,* HarperCollins, New York, 1988)

For me it has been more than a little heart-breaking to discover how persistent these false ideas are, and how profoundly they have shaped our own present-day experiences of our menstrual cycles. In my Luna House workshops age-old prejudices resurface in countless and startlingly virulent ways in the things women believe about themselves, both consciously and unconsciously. Our studies begin by exploring what we first learned about menstrual cycles. While there are, thankfully, always a few welcome exceptions – women whose foremothers have somehow managed to preserve and hand down to them a positive view – the words that most frequently go up on the whiteboard include those shown below – and in fifteen years of these workshops, I have seen very few occasions when either 'shame' or 'embarrassment' were not in first place on this list of women's spontaneous words describing their experience.

Ashamed
Embarrassed
Scared it will show
"the curse"
Secret
Intolerant
Don't talk about it
Bloating
Not "normal"
Guilty
so angry
Over-the-top emotions
everything is too hard
Lose all my patience
just want everyone and everything to GO AWAY
a punishment
pain
wish it didn't have to happen
anxious about everything
try not to think about it
tears, tears, tears
A necessary evil
feeling all wrong
can't stand myself
stops me doing stuff
just put up with it
RAGE
Madness
don't believe anything I say
depressed
crazy thoughts
tired
so changeable!!!
the bitch from hell
grounds for divorce
not-being-told-anything
always keeping it silent
so alone
just learning how to use the stuff to keep it all hidden
Pretend its not happening
a secret blight in my life
out of control
no energy
irritable
hiding it

Deeply erroneous ideas about women and their menstruality have been perpetrated for so long, by such influential figures, and across such broad spectrums in history, that even the most extreme and outrageous of them have been mistaken for truth and gone unchallenged. For somewhere between 250 and 300 generations much of the world has

ed women's ways inferior to men's, and held menstruality to be the root cause of female disability. Over such a length of time these damaging misperceptions have acted like a subliminal commentary, leaching out of women our ability to feel and sustain an **internal** point of reference telling us what we are and what is true about us. Lacking this, we have become (and remain today) all too susceptible to believing that a life without menstruality is more 'normal' than one which is constantly disrupted by the shifts and changes our female hormones produce.

Almost all of the world's major religions have demonised menstruality – and particularly menstruation – in various ways, expressing abhorrence and connotations of sin, guilt, impurity, punishment, abomination and contamination in their sacred texts. And it has fared no better in the secular world. Aristotle himself declared that *'we must look upon the female character as being a sort of natural deficiency'*[15] and by the time of Christ the famous Roman scholar Pliny was introducing the discourse on menstruation in his Encyclopaedia of Natural History with the declaration: *'Hardly can there be found a thing more monstrous than is that flux and course of theirs'.*[16] Pliny then goes on to describe in detail the catastrophes that will occur in the mere presence of a woman *'during the times of this their sickness'* … which include wine going sour, crops withering in the field, fruit falling from trees; tools, knives and swords losing their sharpness, bees dying in the hive, iron and steel rusting with a *'filthy, strong and poysoned stink, if they lay but hand thereupon'*, and dogs going mad. In the agricultural societies of the times, pronouncements such as this from a source so authoritative would have devastated any chance of political or social standing for women. It can easily be seen that only a short step was required from these beliefs to the declarations of witchcraft which were soon to be the death warrant of millions of menstrual women.

Moreover, the massive tomes of Pliny had already served as **the** unquestionable authority on medical matters, including *'this pernicious mischief'* [menstruation] for more than 1000 years at the time the catholic church began training male physicians in medicine

---

15   Aristotle, *On the Generation of Animals*, 350BC. Aristotle was a great thinker, whose ideas are foundational to western civilisation – however he was firmly convinced of the inferiority of women and this assumption runs through much of his thought and writing.

16   Pliny's *Natural History* in Philemon's translation. Selected by Paul Turner. Centaur Classics. Centaur Press, 1962, p 83-84

as we know it today. Regrettably, his 'expertise' formed the rock-solid foundation of what has been regarded as medical knowledge about women, so it is little wonder menstruality has been considered an illness, a disability, a maladaptation, or an unnecessary evil right up into our own times.

In terms of menstruality's inclusion in ordinary records of life over the centuries, it is strikingly absent from mention in history, geography, biography, art and literature – a perfect replica of the bizarre anomaly we live in today, where menstruality is present on a daily basis in half the world's population, but is nowhere to be seen or heard. And yet, as humanity progressed into more 'enlightened' times, and women began to demand their right to inclusion in areas such as higher education, workplace equality and political participation, menstruality was commonly used as a reason for excluding them – with strong backup from the medical profession, which had by now well and truly replaced religion as the source of indisputable truths. Women were routinely confined in asylums for *'the Natural Weaknesses'* and *'Secret Distempers Peculiarly Incident to Them'*[17] and Harley Street's most famous pioneering psychiatrist[18] declared: *'The monthly activity of the ovaries… has a notable effect upon the mind and body, wherefore it may become an important cause of mental and physical derangement. Most women at that time* [menstruation] *are susceptible, irritable and capricious, any cause of vexation affecting them more seriously than usual, and some who have the insane neurosis exhibit a disturbance of mind which amounts almost to a disease'.*

We are faced with an unresolvable dilemma as we try to take our place in society: on the one hand we are bombarded with information and advertising that tells us our menstrual cycle is a disorder that needs medication and alteration so that we can function 'normally'; while on the other we are given the clear message that it is perfectly natural and we should carry on regardless and never expect any allowances to be made for it. We are left no alternative except shame and a sense of personal failure if our menstruality

---

17   A 1727 medical reference book carried the daunting title: *A Rational Account of the Natural Weaknesses of Women and of Secret Distempers peculiarly Incident to Them,* with a later edition tellingly specifying that the Secret Distempers referred to are those afflicting *The Female Sex from Eleven years of Age to Fifty or Upwards.*
18   Henry Maudsley, *Sex in Mind and Education,* 1873

does cause fluctuations in our energy, inclination or availability for work, productivity, sport, sex, domestic duties, the demands of life, or a consistently cheerful, energetic and gracious attitude.

Sadly, even much of the feminism we have known in recent centuries has been curiously compromised in its attitudes to menstrual cycles, and perhaps more trapped than it has realised in centuries-old prejudices. Instead of campaigning for our right to a life that *suits* our cyclical nature – a truly feminine life that would not ask us to deny, compromise or adapt our real selves – feminists, in their very understandable desire for equality with men, strove to achieve it by denying that our menstruality affects us. A feminist campaigning in 1874 for women's entry to the medical profession wrote *'healthy women do as a rule disregard [our periods] almost completely'*[19].

We should look carefully at this argument, because it is still as topical as ever, and we may well be inclined to agree with it. But rather than insisting that our workplaces, educational and professional institutions, sports arenas, political, cultural and social conventions be adjusted to accommodate women as we really are, this approach only increases the pressure on us to be the ones to hide, deny and override the voices of our cycle, as if agreeing with everything in history that tells us menstruality makes us inferior or disabled, and has no place in public life. The only way to get ahead as women, it would seem, is to give up, or at least overcome, the very thing that makes us female!

In our desperation not to be hindered by our 'troublesome' femaleness we were all too susceptible to the next, and still current, advance in the oppression of menstruality: hormone-blaming. Long deprived of authentic knowledge about how our hormones are designed to work *on their own terms*, it is perhaps not surprising that feminists welcomed the seeming breakthrough of fake hormones that could eliminate our menstrual cycles and our fertility, as the gateway to emancipation. The tragedy of feminism's blindness, and its unfortunate legacy for young women today, is our failure to see that 'women's liberation' needed not to be from the 'shackles' of our own biology, but from the cultural setup that made it impossible for us to flourish **in** that biology. Hormone-blaming has

---

19   Medical student Elizabeth Garrett Anderson, rebutting Henry Maudsley in the *Fortnightly Review* of May 1874. Elizabeth was a most admirable and courageous pioneer of women's rights and her stance shows us how hard women had to fight exclusion on the grounds of the menstruality.

to be one of the most disabling and short-sighted errors ever made. It creates in women an abiding fear that our own bodies will betray us; that our femaleness is treacherous and makes us misfits. From a profound distrust of our feminine hormones, it is only one short step to the alarmingly widespread notion that we are far better off without our menstrual cycles.

The belief that women's menstruality is a design fault has been around in spoken and unspoken forms for a long, long time – and let's face it, most of us have probably felt that way about it ourselves on occasion. The venom of this conviction has taken many forms over the ages, denouncing us as possessed, deranged, dangerous, evil, inferior, polluting, unclean, diseased, untrustworthy, complicated, capricious, hormonally afflicted, mad, bad and sad because of our monthly changeability. The faith humanity has placed in believing there is a chemical solution to every problem has seen the development of the apparently most efficacious, but in reality most disempowering, response we could ever make to menstruality. Our determination to 'fix' – alter, suppress or even eliminate – all that challenges our masculinist way of living life has almost caused menstruality to disappear from view altogether, as women have been offered, in the appealing guise of sophistication, more and more means of not experiencing it. By the end of the 20th century promoters were offering us the glossy prospect of freedom, control and an enhanced quality of life by relieving us altogether of the messy, inconvenient and *unnecessary* bother of menstruating. It is indescribably sad that so many women these days have so little real knowledge about their cycles that we are easily persuaded to believe the claims of those who profit greatly by convincing us that our cycles are a primitive, obsolete, redundant or, even more insultingly, *unhealthy* encumbrance that we really should have evolved out of by now.

As cultural attitudes cause us to find our menstrual cycles increasingly inconvenient in today's supposedly emancipated lives, huge numbers of women have unquestioningly flocked to their doctors' offices to be saved from Nature by science. So convinced are we by now that fake hormones are better for us than our real ones, that in parts of the world we routinely take hormonal menstruality-suppressing medication, with no idea of what it was our original hormones were designed to create in the first place. In this way we unwittingly join the cultural resistance that traps us, and continue living such adapted lives that we literally do not know who we really are.

The good news is, though, that all is not lost. Indeed, thanks to the liberations we have already achieved, we are in a better position than ever before to take our final steps to freedom – freedom to be fully female *and* equal. However, if we are to untangle ourselves from a history deeply flawed by ignorance and fear-fuelled prejudice we will need fresh eyes to look through – eyes that look inward rather than outward; eyes that can see in the dark of a long history of obscurity to rediscover what *is* true about us. We will need enough insight (inner sight) to liberate us from the blindness we have been taught, and the confidence to question everything we see, hear and feel around us regarding our menstrual cycles, so that we can step outside assumptions that have too long been mistaken for facts. Invisible to us because of their familiarity, these wrong beliefs keep us from experiencing the femenome as it really is. My hope is that the rest of this book will help you find the simple (but not always easy) keys toward seeing yourself, through the kaleidoscopic viewfinder of your menstrual cycle, in a whole new light.

CHAPTER TWO

How our inheritance shapes our experience

> The legacy of women: cultural resistance internalised as personal resistance

To resist something is to obstruct its natural flow, to refuse to engage with it, or to inhibit its full and free expression. Many cultures in the world resist their women's menstrual cycles in ways that can be blatant and deliberate, or subtle and unconscious.

Cultural resistance

Cultural resistance is easy to miss because we are so steeped in it. It feels, and quite literally is, completely normal. We are so familiar with its assumptions that we tend never to question them. And so attuned to its demands that *we* feel wrong if we have trouble meeting them.

> We are so filled with the historical dislike and distrust of the feminine that it feels quite ok and normal to dislike and distrust it in ourselves

Cultural resistance says, in a thousand unstated but very powerful ways, that menstruality should not get in the way, has nothing to contribute, and needs to be kept out of public life. Its unspoken edicts continue into our current times the 5000 year old story that menstrual cycles are a disability, an impediment to getting on with the things that matter. That they should be kept out of sight, out of mind, and preferably out of body too.[20]

> Cultural resistance includes everything **around us** that expects and requires us to live as if our menstrual cycles were not happening

Many women believe the old taboo has disappeared. In the western world at least, we do indeed *appear* to accept the reality of menstruation quite openly and even supportively. We fill our supermarket shelves and pharmacies with menstrual products, and advertise them graphically on TV. But look more closely, and you will see how cleverly cultural resistance makes itself invisible, and thus so readily absorbed into women's secret feelings about themselves…

> While we publically acknowledge that women do menstruate we simultaneously perpetuate an aura of shamefulness and undesirability around that by promoting products and devices that hide and deny our periods to make it seem that they don't exist

It is tempting to believe we have achieved equality in the workplace and in public life. But how many women would tell a prospective employer at a job interview that they would be taking five days off each month for their period? Or run for political or public office with a campaign slogan promising to allow at least three menstrual cycles to consider important decisions? Women are often the first, and the loudest, to claim that our work performance is not affected by our menstruality, no matter how much our private, interior experience may suggest otherwise. We have had to be. We know that the terms of our hard-won admission

---

20   In an article in *The Guardian* newspaper in July 2019 a leading expert in women's health for Britain's Royal College of GPs states that '*there is no health benefit to [menstruating]. Ninety-nine per cent of women don't need to bleed',* while a London professor of sexual and reproductive health adds '*…it seems like one of God's great design faults… it is not helpful to have these periods…*' Nicola Davis, '*We don't need to bleed':* *why many women are giving up on periods*, The Guardian, 18.10.19.

the world within women

to the positions we have gained are that we do not bring our capricious and troublesome menstrual cycle with us or expect it to be tolerated in a commercial economy that has more important things to get on with.

Under these conditions it is no surprise that women dread and despise certain aspects of their menstruality nature, see little or no value in it, and feel bad about themselves because of it. While we're all trying so hard to conform to the great cultural lie that it's better not to experience our menstrual cycle – that it's more 'advanced' or sophisticated to do away with its 'intrusions' into our daily life – each woman sensing its vivid and inescapable presence within her feels personally at fault for being unable to live up to that lie. This is a mega- epidemic of our times, the dis-ease of **internalised resistance**, absorbed into every woman's body and mind by osmosis from the pressure around her that she need not, and should not, 'suffer from' menstrual cycles. We may think the menstrual banishments of old no longer apply to us, but they have simply been refined into a much more subtle and sophisticated form that makes them hard to detect. These days we need no overt prohibitions to keep our menstruality at bay, for we have learned to do that ourselves. By unspoken collective agreement, and by innumerable means that we need to wake up to, we banish our menstruality as much as we can from notice, and even from our own awareness. We compliantly oblige everyone by turning up for our lives without it.

> The menstrual taboo has not disappeared. We no longer notice its presence **because we have internalised it**, obediently imposing it on ourselves

Another form of cultural resistance, although we may not recognise it as such, is our tolerance of a proliferation of endocrine-disrupting substances in our environment – pesticides, herbicides, plastics, artificial foods and drinks, cosmetics, electro-magnetic radiation and other pollutants. We know these things harm our hormones, but we are not outraged. We accept them because the corporate profit-motive they serve is collectively agreed to be a higher priority than human health and wellbeing. Our co-option into cultural resistance has taught us that hormones just don't matter enough to be safeguarded in everyday life.

We should never blame ourselves for being caught up in cultural resistance. We are all in it together, and for now it is the only 'reality' we have. While the femenome's real design and purpose are still unknown to us we cannot see that something is missing, and it is virtually impossible for us not to be captured by the compelling logic of the status quo. Ignorance breeds ignore-ance, and we have developed an astounding capacity to ignore our sensitive inner voices, to bear our suffering unquestioningly, to believe it is what we deserve. Like tender plants, uprooted from their native ecology and transplanted into foreign soils, we have adapted to conditions that are unsuited to us. We are deeply accustomed to the vague discomforts of not-fitting, of striving against our inner sensations, of over-riding our sensitivities.

From this place it may take us a little time, and our own very conscious permission, to begin to recognise that what is familiar around us is not necessarily what is true about us or right for us. To look for a starting place, you may find it helpful to go back to the deep feminine memory of menstruality-inclusiveness at the beginning of chapter one (page 21), and take a long, slow breath into your belly…

What would it be like to live in a society where everything was set up to maximise, appreciate, value and harmonise with our cycles?

where we would be provided with time out and special accommodations for our (communal) monthly bleeding, with everything supplied for our care and comfort?

where every dark moon week was a happily anticipated public holiday, and ovulation time a celebration of energy, productivity and sexuality?

where our intuitions, wisdom, dreams and desires would be sought after and respected as the most compelling guidance for all social and political decision-making?

where sensitivity, spirituality, emotional feelings, tenderness, love, nurturance and care for all life would be of paramount importance?

the world within women

where all of our monthly changes would be understood, welcomed, shared and supported?

where we would be esteemed, admired, loved, because of them?

Better yet, gather with other women to daydream and imagine, envision and intuit such a way of life. The more we can share our sense of what *could* be, the more we create and co-create what *will* be.

a pause to consider...

Allow yourself to start noticing all the different forms of cultural resistance working around you in everyday life (everything around us that asks us to live as if our menstrual cycle was not happening). Activate your resistance-detecting antennae when you are out shopping, listening to and watching media, having conversations, playing sport, being a mum. Pay attention to overt and covert messages about menstruality in products and medications; in advertising. To spoken and unspoken assumptions in scientific and medical publications. To doctors' advice and prescriptions. To workplace expectations, job descriptions and ideal-applicant attributes. To political norms and values, including feminist ones. To social etiquette. To role models and examples set up by your culture. Are these menstruality-inclusive, or menstruality-exclusive? Let your eyes and ears pick up on absences of menstruality acknowledgement, as well as on any negativity in attitudes to it.

This may not be easy at first. Look for very normal assumptions that expect you to live as if you did not have a menstrual cycle. And things provided to ensure that your menstrual cycle does not 'get in the way of' your activities and levels of functioning all around the month. Name them, and see if you can imagine and describe how they would need to be different if allowance was to be made for our cycles.

To help us do this, we may need to develop our ability to imagine and design a menstruality-inclusive society (as envisaged in the exercise above). If your menstruality is affected in any way by medical or environmental factors, do include your particular needs in these considerations. Take your time and dare to trust your real inner wishes, even if they seem far from possible.

Let this be a gradual awakening for you. Begin now, and then return to this exercise often as you learn more about the real dimensions and potentials of your menstrual cycle in the coming chapters. Add to your design as your awareness grows. The notes and drawings you make will help you identify small and large adjustments you might like to make in your own way of allowing your cycle more importance in your life.

And together, as we all learn how to see through the resistance and open to a woman-centred approach to everything, what we write and draw in response to these exercises will become the creative foundations we need for evolving a very different society. Imagine that!

Be gentle as you do this. The more aware we become, the more grief and outrage we will feel about just how much we are expected to override and ignore what is happening inside us, every day of every month.

How does cultural resistance become personal resistance?

Adapting ourselves to life within the *culture* of resistance demands that each woman cultivates her own *personal* menstruality resistance so she can comply with the expectations she will encounter. She is to preserve her menstrual cycle for reproductive purposes, but to keep it out of the way at all other times. Do we ever stop to consider what this actually asks of us, or have we by sheer necessity become so adept at it that we do not even notice it is costing us dearly?

Recognising and healing our personal menstrual cycle resistance will ask us to undertake a care-full process of disentanglement, identifying and discarding, one by one, the strands

the world within women

of inherited prejudice that have penetrated our own intimate daily dialogue with our cycle. This is far from easy. What we need to remember at all times is that

> We did not create menstruality resistance. We inherited it.
> **Personal menstruality resistance**
> **IS NOT OUR FAULT**

so that we can stay patient, loving, realistic, respectful and curious as we seek to change our unintentional resistance into conscious self-support.

Personal resistance includes everything we have to do to pretend our menstrual cycle is not happening, or is not affecting us: all our well-intentioned efforts, both conscious and unconscious, to deny, minimise, override, control, alter, suppress, ignore, hide, eliminate, manipulate, avoid or 'improve upon' our secret experiences of it. In short, everything that prevents us from knowing, trusting and living our cycle as it really is.

For women whose menstruality is a source of suffering because of severe pain, endometriosis, heightened pre-menstrual distress or any other of the host of conditions which sadly affect so many of us, the predicament is even more acute. When our cycle is affected by medical or other factors, especially those which make it impossible to maintain unbroken attendance at work or study, we are that much more exposed to the lack of acknowledgement and support that all women face. It is completely understandable that the sheer necessity of coping in a world where there are few opportunities for monthly time-out forces us to hone our resistance skills very highly. If this is your experience, your situation is one of double jeopardy and I would ask you to read the following pages with utmost compassion for yourself, gently adapting what is offered to your particular situation as much as may be possible. For you it is an even more delicate task to separate and soften out the layers of resistance that *can* be eliminated once they are understood. May you find, with us all, some alternative ways to take care of yourself (such as those described later in this book) and lessen the suffering even if we cannot yet eliminate it.

Personal resistance can take many forms, and we need to attend to them all if we are to truly open to the life our hormones intend for us. Let's imagine we wake up one morning just starting to bleed. But it's Monday, and we have to be at work in an hour! What are some of the things we have to do to manage that?

> Personal resistance is everything we have to do **inside ourselves** to pretend our menstrual cycle isn't happening and ensure it doesn't get in the way of our 'real life'

Physical resistance

If our menstruality is bringing us pain, fatigue, discomfort or sensitive emotions, but we have to get on with our day as best we can, we will inevitably tense or tighten our muscles to some degree in order to over-ride how we feel and do what is expected of us. We have many ways of demanding this of ourselves: 'pull yourself together', 'get a grip', 'harden up', 'get over it', 'get on with it', 'put on a brave face', 'stop feeling sorry for yourself', 'tough it out', 'just put up with it', 'grin and bear it' – an endless repertoire. When we stop and listen to exactly **how** we manage to pretend our menstruality is not happening, we will probably find **constriction** somewhere in our body. 'Soldiering on' asks for that kind of **bracing**. We women are habitual stoics.

So the next thing to pay close attention to is the effect this has on our breathing. It's hard to have a free and easy flow of breath through our body while we're holding pain, sensation, shame, resentment or tiredness at bay, or pushing ourselves to do something that is at odds with our true state of energy. Even the most subtle muscular holding constrains our breath, making it faster and shallower.

What else do we do physically, with the best of intentions, to cope with our secret menstruality suffering? Do we need medications to get through our affected days? Necessary and beneficial as these may be, they are the paramount tools of resistance, because they keep us believing that menstruality should be changed to make us fit for work, rather than that work should be changed to allow us to be fit for menstruality. Do we walk differently, sit differently, hold ourselves together differently? Do we *cover up* our real feelings at our tricky menstruality times? How important is it to us to keep our menstruality a secret, to maintain the appearance that it is not happening to us? What lengths do we go to in order to achieve this, even if they are so automatic we hardly notice them? And, do we give ourselves credit for doing all this and making no fuss – or have we always just regarded it as 'normal' and no cause for complaint?

> Menstruality resistance asks us to **carry on regardless** … that is, **without regard for the femenome trying to speak inside us**

Mental resistance

What are our **thoughts** on that Monday morning as we wake up feeling menstruality's presence in our body and facing the prospect of a day at the office or in front of a class of rowdy children? Women live with the constant, unacknowledged tension of having to choose between 'normal' life that says '*No menstruality allowed: shape up or ship out*', and the very different one we would be living if we *were* allowed to take our cycle's presence into account. Indeed the very thing we say or feel inside ourself as we struggle to get out of bed, or drag our tears back inside our eyes by sheer force of will, may well be 'I have no choice'.

Even thoughts as ordinary as 'it's a hassle' or 'I wish it hadn't come today' are enough to produce a negative signal in our energy field, which in turn stimulates a subtle clamping down of our mind as it goes into 'cope' or 'manage' mode. This mental tightening can take up residence around our mouth or jaw as a clench, or between our eyebrows as a frown, setting up an internal resoluteness, or a psychological 'girding of loins' that is all too easily translated into a physical one. Our self-talk may become severe, negative, impatient or self-critical as we enter hormonal states that don't sit easily with what our diary demands.

Mental resistance will inevitably happen when we are so infused with common beliefs that we *use them as a starting point for our own attitudes to menstruality.* We resist and override our inner world because we believe it is not valid. We constantly tell ourselves we have to adapt, cope, manage, *press on.* That the outer world is more valid, more right, makes more sense. Mental resistance calls for a resolute focus on how we believe we *should be* functioning, rather than on how we actually *are* functioning. It is a constant striving to set our compass bearing to external points of reference, to the menstruality-free male model of life. This means not being who we are.

> Mental resistance calls for a resolute focus on how we believe we **should be** functioning rather than on how we actually **are** functioning

Emotional resistance

Emotional resistance can show up as feelings of dread, worry or dislike; regarding our menstruality as the enemy, feeling embarrassed about it, or keeping it a shame-tinged secret. Almost all of the women I have worked with at Luna House carry negative feelings about their pre-menstrual phase, and mixed feelings, at best, in relation to menstruating. Emotional resistance can take the form of negativity, where we adopt a negative, conflicted and combatant relationship with what our menstruality brings to us, and actually pit our energy against it.

When we are afraid of or annoyed by something, we tend to pull back from it, withdraw, do whatever we can to put a safe distance between it and us. We want to change it into something more acceptable, to get a sense we can control it. It is not easy in the face of something frightening to step forward in genuine curiosity to see what it truly is, and what we might learn from it – and sadly there is very little support available at this time for women who might wish to engage with, rather than resist, their menstruality.

Shame is especially important to be aware of in considering our subtle emotional responses to menstruality. Shame is one of the major and most costly menstruality resistances. For example, many women feel explosively angry or guilt-stricken if someone suggests they may be pre-menstrual. It is like a switch that sends our self-esteem plummeting and cuts us off from the validity of our inner experience. In shame we invest our attention into hiding our reality, and are therefore unavailable to experience ourselves as we actually are. Shame compresses our breath and our vitality. It produces an energetic contraction that is physiological, psychological, emotional and spiritual, all at once.

Energetic and spiritual resistance

Energetic resistance is all about denial and over-riding our menstruality states, and the re-investment or diversion of our energy, awareness and attention into what we have been taught matters more. Think for a moment about the extent to which you are able to accomplish this feat (out of sheer necessity) and you will probably be astounded. Sadly, the better we get at doing this, the more we are helping to create and sustain the illusion that a menstruality-free world works a whole lot better than the one that would let us be honest. Energetic resistance is so easily self-perpetuating until we see through it.

Energetic resistance is really like holding our menstruality against ourselves, quite literally. Because *we* are unintentionally working against *its* natural flow, we unfortunately get the impression that our menstruality is working against *us* instead of for us. Under pressure to keep our unruly feminine changes and intensities 'under control', we hold them tightly, trying to ensure they don't leak out. We are simultaneously struggling to keep these troublesome energies close to us so they won't disgrace us or be seen by others, and push them away because we don't want to feel them.

The femenome is by nature a spiritual energy. Spiritual resistance is disengagement, or disconnection from what our soul is trying to show us through our menstruality. We learn to detach or avoid experiencing what is happening inside us: a *finely honed refusal to let our menstruality have its say.* Our spiritual resistance is expressed energetically in habits we all know well: ignoring, not keeping track or acknowledging, not allowing our menstrual cycle to matter enough to give it a place in our life. Shrugging it off. Paying it no attention. Making plans without taking it into account. Not caring about it. Many women these days do not know where they are in their cycle, and are therefore unable to make sense of the ways it affects them. We are all supremely trained in this subtle form of resistance – in fact it has been explicitly and implicitly modelled to us all our lives as a necessary virtue we should strive to acquire.

> The energy we have been taught to invest in resistance is then not available for the designer life our hormones want us to live

Resistance of relinquishment

There is one further energetic resistance we need to pay close attention to – perhaps, once we recognise it, the most heart-breaking of all. It is, quite simply, **the resistance of giving up on ourselves**. We do not mean to do this – much of the time we do not realise we are doing it, and certainly we have been led to believe we have no alternative. The Feminine inside of us will constantly find ways through our menstruality's voices to remind us of all that is fine, deep, sensitive and soulful – and *explicitly feminine* – within us. Yet we just do not expect these aspects to be accepted, included or allowed in daily life – so we simply and routinely relinquish them, believing that in 'the real world' we have to harden up and do without them. Be gentle as you begin to notice exactly what, and how much, you routinely give up on in the **resistance of relinquishment**.

$$\sim\!\diamondsuit\!\sim$$

The important thing to know is that, subtle as they are, all our micro-forms of resistance – those tiny tightenings – affect our breathing and cost us more than we may realise. When we don't breathe *in* fully, we cannot be adequately nourished by oxygen. We are less energised. And we are not properly engaged in our life – our Self is not wholly present, aware and awake within us, so we are living semi-consciously or even unconsciously. And if the constriction of resistance stops us breathing *out* fully we can never really relax, surrender, let go and enjoy the rest pause at the bottom of our breath.

> When our consciousness or soul is not fully present in our life we leave energetic vacuums that make it much easier for distress, illness, imbalance or fatigue to take up residence in our system

Menstruality resistance is a real predicament for women. It splits our will and connection away from the natural energy of our cycle and pits the two against each other in a wild and unresolvable distress I call *ricochet resistance*.

Ricochet Resistance

At pre-menstruation and menstruation, our cycle will pull us **inward**, away from the world and the needs of others, to attend to ourself. But we resist this because **the culture and the structure of our life** say that is the wrong priority: *we must not!*

However, we also resist all demands to go **outward**, because our **menstruality** says we haven't got the energy for that: *we cannot!*

And so we are caught in an impossible, intolerable, no-win, double-bind resistance. Our energy cannot flow. It bounces insanely and erratically within this squash court of barriers, making us feel crazy, frustrated, sped-up, volatile. All this energy that has nowhere to go except into ricocheting escalation, makes us turn on ourself – in irritation, volcanic feelings, and, most vexing of all, a conviction that something is terribly wrong with us.

It is this unresolvable predicament – not hormones themselves – that creates the artificial speediness, emotional distress and feelings of 'craziness' that so many women experience in their PMS (premenstrual syndrome) or PMT (premenstrual tension) times.

Ricochet resistance burns up vast reservoirs of female energy – energy that is actually designed for sacred and transformational purposes.

a pause to reflect...

What are the things you most commonly say to yourself about your menstrual cycle?

Write them down. Be honest.

When in your cycle do you say them? What provokes them?

What do you like most about your menstrual cycle? Why?

What do you like least about it? Why?

Becoming aware: what are your personal menstrual cycle resistances?

If you look with a gentle and non-judgemental eye at your month, what menstruality resistances might you see: Over-riding? Ignoring? Disliking? Tension or holding in your body? Carrying on regardless? Expecting a lot of yourself? Grumpiness? Resentment? Breathing alterations? Negative self-talk? Self-blame for not fitting in? Holding tight in pain? Relinquishing what you really feel or want? … Anything else?

What would those 'negative' feelings be trying to bring to your attention if you really listened to them?

What would your life feel like if you could allow, rather than relinquish, your real feelings ·and needs?

What adjustments would you need to make in your body / thoughts / expectations / emotional responses / spiritual life, to reduce or be free of your resistances?

What parts of you and your life need more awareness, love, support, inclusion, care and understanding so that you can be less resistant?

Do remember: *menstruality resistance is not our fault!* It is inevitable in a culture that makes no allowance for menstruality. Be loving, realistic, respectful and creative as you seek to change your unintentional resistance into self-support.

PART TWO

Re-Orienting
ourselves to a new way of knowing

CHAPTER THREE

Learning to look through a femenome lens

A yes to the quest of conscious menstruality will ask us to open to a tender and delicate journey, and possibly to step into a different relationship with our self than we have ever considered before. It will take us on a rarely trodden path, where the only signposts are written in a language we have never been taught to read: that of our deeply distrusted hormones.

The art of conscious menstruality is to become very simple in our enquiry. If our beginning place is to accept that women are made to a perfect design just as they are, a new curiosity can wake up inside us, ask different questions and hear new answers that science cannot find. We need to cultivate an attitude of *in-nocence* – of not assuming we already know – so that the femenome itself can become our teacher without any pre-conceptions getting in the way. Let's be clear from the start that conscious menstruality is counter-culture. It is not easy to trust or respect something that has been shut out of collective awareness, and indeed disparaged, for so long. It is, in fact, extremely difficult, and it can be a bit lonely too. You may find that many women will not want to accompany you in this approach, preferring the convenience of giving their menstrual cycle as little attention and space in their lives as possible.

Science and medicine, as we have already seen, have long tried to persuade us that our hormones create a lot of problems for us, and need correction – or even replacement – to remedy them. And sadly, the ever-increasing occurrence of endometriosis, polycystic ovary syndrome, dysmenorrhea (painful periods), amenorrhea (absence of periods) and all manner of pre-menstrual and menstrual ills *does* present a very concerning picture that seems to justify that belief. How strange and alarming it is that this does not give rise to a new question: not *what is wrong* **with** *women that they suffer so much?* But *what is wrong* **for** *women that makes their hormones so frequently troubled?* Not, *how do menstrual cycles make us suffer?* But *how do we make our menstrual cycles suffer?* Like the canaries that old-time miners used to take underground as a warning signal (if the canary died in its cage it showed that the mine's air was toxic) the epidemic levels of menstrual cycle and menopause distress suffered by women in our times are crying out for recognition that our current environments and cultural norms are toxic for us.

So here is a crucial re-orientation:

> It is resistance that distresses our hormones
> not hormones that make menstruality distressing

and to understand this any further we will need to become very, very interested in our hormones, and why they behave as they do.

Menstruality hormones – agents of the soul

Many processes in our body are regulated by hormones. Hormones, as we know, can at first glance seem somewhat mysterious in their ways of doing things. If we want to understand them we will need to look further (or perhaps closer in) than the view of medicine and science, which has tended to separate body from soul and see human beings almost as animated machines. In paying attention only to the mechanism and not to *what animates it* we overlook the clues that can lead us to the missing pieces of the puzzle of what we really are.

> If we attend only to the mechanisms of our body and not to what animates
> it we disregard important clues to how we are really designed to function

Have we ever paused to wonder about the location of the three glands governing our menstruality hormones: pituitary, hypothalamus and pineal? They all sit in the base of our brain, placing them within the area recognised by major and ancient knowledge systems as the third eye chakra; the seat of the soul, of inner-seeing, of intuition – our window into consciousness, and the portal between physical and spiritual life. So, what are these feminine hormones of ours really designed to do? What might there be to trust?

> Our hormones are not designed to obstruct our lives or make them difficult but to invite us into **greater consciousness**

We know from experience that our hormones are exquisitely sensitive and finely tuned. That they work with minuteness, precision and balance. That they cannot be fooled or coerced. That they respond to everything. We may have noticed that they fluctuate according to our stress levels, to changes in our lives, to travelling across time zones and through magnetic fields. Our menstruality hormones know what is needed for our growth, development and wellbeing *as a woman.* They are like the executive officers of the soul, programmed to carry out its blueprint for the natural *feminine* life we are designed to be living. And that life, of course, includes things our history says do not fit or cannot be had in 'the real world'.

So what if our hormones are a highly-attuned internal guidance-system operating with more sophistication than science has yet discovered between our spiritual, emotional, mental and physical spheres of life? What if they have the capacity to function as a kind of watchdog, or a super-sensitive warning system, alerting us to ways in which culture tries to over-ride or deny our nature and stop us from listening to what our menstruality is telling us? For example, most women have been trained to believe they should not allow their cycle or menopausal events to interfere with their working day. Our hormones, therefore, have had to devise ways to make these important facts of feminine life **un**deniable and **un**avoidable by creating physical, emotional and mental reminders that really do force us to take notice. There is nothing like a menstrual cramp or hot flush to remind a woman she *is* a woman, whatever role she is endeavouring to fulfil, and to jolt her into considering

she is acting with fidelity to her femaleness or trying to keep it a secret from herself
s everyone else.

..... same time as our culture tells us we cannot have or be these uniquely feminine ways, our hormones are insisting that they are *just what we inherently need*. And this is why it is in our most 'hormonal' times (puberty, pre-menstruation and menopause) that the parts of ourselves we have been taught to disown, bury, avoid or leave out of awareness suddenly make themselves felt. These aspects of us – strong feelings, fears and worries, deep needs, important desires – want us to know they *are* there, and they *do* matter.

So it may well be that our hormones' specific job description is to keep reminding us what is trying to happen, and needing to happen, in 'the real world' of our natural womanhood. That menstruality hormones are *truth regulators,* whose function is to keep us connected to the most essential facets of our Self, no matter how much we are pressured to override them.[21] As carriers and catalysts of the femenome's original template inside us, of course our hormones will feel acutely the graunching and jarring where that feminine nature rubs painfully up against a way of life that has been designed and perpetuated to exclusively suit a masculine ethos! Why would this surprise us or cause us to lose faith in hormonal howls of protest?

If we are not aware of our hormones and their real purpose for us, it is easy to feel overtaken and controlled by them. The more we try to resist their messages and hold on to what society says is acceptable (trying to be good women by carrying on regardless) the more our hormones will do their job of disrupting that pretence, so that we *have to* open up to the consciousness our menstruality is offering us.

> Our hormones do not cause, or ask for, **trouble**.
> They cause, and ask for, **awareness**.

---

21   I acknowledge my initiation into this awareness, which I have since further developed, as Penelope Shuttle and Peter Redgrave's proposal: '*Suppose that society is a lie, and the period is a moment of truth which will not sustain lies*' in The Wise Wound: Menstruation and Everywoman, Revised Edition, Paladin, 1986, p 56-58.

In cultures which are resistant to the changes of womanly life, our hormones may need to be literally *out of control* so that they can do their work of inviting us *beyond* society's control. This may sound frightening, but once we begin to understand that menstruality hormones have a beautiful logic all of their own, we may wish to reconsider whether keeping them 'under control' is really what we want, and indeed, whose control that would be!

a pause to reflect...

What do the often-used phrases 'out of control' and 'under control' evoke for you?

If your hormonal life was to be **out of**

control

what would you like it to be **in**, *instead?*

What might better hold and contain such a delicate and sensitive part of you than the rigid box called 'control':

What might support your hormonal life, and allow it to be itself, if it was out of the box?

What would you trust, if your hormones wanted to escape from the confines of control?

Love? Freedom? Trust Itself? Consciousness? Truth? Soul? Their own guidance? The Laws of Nature? The grace of the Divine Feminine?

It takes courage and ingenuity to live in accordance with our hormones **and it is immensely and uniquely rewarding.**

How does resistance affect our hormones?

As long as the femenome has no name and the terms of 'normal' participation in society require us to live as if menstruality were not occurring, we are all compelled to live in a state of chronic resistance *to our femaleness*. The only way we can truly become free of the blight of compulsory self-resistance will be to have public and normalised prioritising, provision and support for menstruality – and while we can hope that will be coming soon, and prepare ourselves to help create it, we don't have it yet. So it is imperative now, if we are to become pioneers of reinstating the femenome, to go a little deeper in understanding just how resistance impacts on our hormones in subtle yet game-changing ways, shutting down functions we didn't even know they had.

Whenever we tighten in resistance – physically, mentally, emotionally or spiritually – we create pressure in our body's energy system. Such is the delicacy of our hormones' sensitivity that they will be affected by every *feeling* and *response* we have toward our menstrual cycle and its events. It is just not possible to be living in secrecy, dislike, discomfort, disconnection, over-ride, bracing or carrying-on-regardless (even if these responses are so subtle or so familiar that we don't consciously notice them) without altering our breathing. As we have already seen, the body tension of resistance shortens and quickens our in-breath and disallows the relaxation of a full out-breath. And of course any change in the depth and pace of our breathing will impact immediately on our ultra-sensitive adrenal system. With more of the stress hormones cortisol and adrenaline rushing to help us through the difficulty they sense we are in, the balance of other hormones is altered in the cascade, and our finely-tuned menstruality mechanisms can no longer function optimally or bring us their gifts.

the world within women

> It is not hormonal imbalance that causes our stress. It is stress that causes our hormonal imbalance. Menstruality resistance is a chronic stress for women.

Pretending, as we have to, that we are not menstrual beings will inevitably create a split in women. It means we do our best to *take our consciousness away from our internal experience*, and apply it very diligently instead to whatever we are required to be doing in the world *outside of ourself.* This leaves a crucial vacuum inside us. With no Self present to take care of them, our pre-menstrual distress or menstrual pain is all we have inside us. Without consciousness, these energies are experienced purely emotionally, or purely physically, and can all too easily come to feel as if they have a life of their own – that they are unwelcome visitors imposing on us, rather than valid and purposeful voices of our own soul trying to guide us to live in a *womanly* way.

> Resisted menstruality is energy without consciousness

Energy without consciousness is like a train off its tracks – it can still bump along in a rough and raw way, but it will not be able to run smoothly to its true destination.

> When our hormones feel out of control it means they are out of consciousness

Unfortunately, too, the tightening of self-resistance triggered by menstruality-averse cultural attitudes tends to create a particular kind of pressure on our pancreas, right in the centre of our bodily sense of self. This affects our insulin production, and in turn other hormonal levels, and also creates the sugar cravings so many women experience, especially pre-menstrually. Our attempts to feel better using chocolate or other stimulants sadly only exacerbate the whole disturbance, as loading our system with sugar overstimulates our adrenals and interferes with our ability to relax and to sleep. It is important to pause and feel what we are really craving as we reach for the chocolate – is it the comforting presence of someone to listen with care and understanding to our genuine but unheard need? Permission to put down the strenuous demands of our life and rest? Or a change in something that is distressing or depleting us?

We have been taught to believe it is our menstruality hormones that create pandemonium inside us – mood swings, extremes of emotion, irritability, pain and fatigue – but none of these *originate* in our endocrine system. To really get ourselves beyond the popular view of hormones as the cause of our menstruality woes, we have to remember that we are more than just physical beings. We are energetically sensitive in ways far beyond what rationality alone can comprehend or measure.

> Our hormones are the mediators between our soul life and our physical life

Our hormones, as the mediators between our soul life and physical life, are trying to reinstate what we have been taught to avoid and ignore. They want to awaken us to the bigger-picture dimensions of what is needed for us to fully be who we are – those layers of our deep nature that we privately know very well, but that science does not acknowledge in us. It is far from easy, of course, to let *in* to our awareness and way of life the very messages we have been trained to keep *out* of our definitions of sanity and normality. This may well require us to take some new and unexpected steps in trust.

> The delicate balance of chemicals and hormones in our body is directly related to how connected or disconnected we are with our Self

Our pituitary and pineal glands secrete different substances in different amounts according to the energetic climate within our body. As we have seen this is calibrated with infinite sensitivity to the degree in which we either connect and respond to our natural feelings or contain and override them. Response keeps our nervous system open and allows *the energy current created by the presence of Self* to keep flowing, so that the delicate and precise functions of our soul-in-body can be optimised. (We will study the art of responding to our

the world within women

feelings in some depth in chapter 7, as the pre-menstrual phase of our cycle purposefully heightens emotions in almost all women.) Where resistance to responding is our default setting (because we have been taught to trust logic over and above emotion) the energy stimulated by our feelings cannot move inside us to allow the resolution it seeks, and the hormonal imbalance resulting from this chronic state of tension does, unfortunately, become established and measurable. It is this that has led to the wrong-way-around interpretation that hormonal imbalance is the *origin* of women's suffering in their menstruality. It is so vitally important for us now to liberate ourselves from this error, and realise that by responding rather than resisting *we can ease and adjust our own hormonal balance* and thrive happily in our menstruality life.

> Hormonal imbalance is not the origin of menstruality problems. Our learned resistance to responding *creates* the hormonal imbalance that distresses our menstruality

Menstruality and sensitivity

Our menstrual cycle is an exquisitely attuned instrument of sensitivity. It *will be* aware, and it *will* respond to everything because it is designed to heighten our consciousness. Unfortunately we are living in cultures dedicated to the suppression of feeling. We medicate feelings, distract them with consumptions and addictions, and develop whole psychologies of managing and controlling them. We have become specialists in minimising, denying and combatting our feelings, often summoning all of our courage and resolve to overcome or contain them. Anything but feel them!

So it is not surprising that we have learned to fear, dread and resist the parts of our menstrual cycle that uncover our feelings in all their raw powerfulness, especially pre-menstruation and menstruation. We are taught that these are times of danger and impairment, when we will need remedies and medications for the disease of feeling our feelings. In cultures where desensitisation is seen as a strength, sensitivity and feeling have come to be viewed as weakness and even pathology.

> The femenome will prompt us in every way it can to restore the essential place of feelings in our individual and collective psyche.

But in its counter-culture way, the femenome is sure to do all it can to restore the essential place of feelings in our individual and collective psyche. It will ask us to engage with the profound sensitivity of our feminine nature, not just with our adapted self. Living in our cultures of desensitisation we are exposed to a constant barrage of artificial and highly manipulated emotion through media 'entertainment' and 'news'. We drench our consciousness and senses with hyper-information and electronic stimuli. We live in a toxic and irradiated environment, and have very few, if any, respites from sensory overload – noise, light, fumes, electromagnetic emissions. We ingest all manner of substances in the guise of food, drink and medicine that are neither natural nor nourishing. Women who suffer from menstruality irregularities or hormonally-related difficulties may well be those who are most sensitive to all these outrages. What if our all too common menstruality-related illnesses are not hormonal malfunctions at all, but a mighty howl of protest at the abuse we are subjected to on a daily basis in the course of our 'normal' lives?

> Conscious menstruality asks us to engage with the profound **sensitivity** of our feminine nature, not just with our adapted self

a pause to reflect...

Sensitivity Checklist

What in your nature is sensitive?

Have you ever been taught to distrust, minimise, deny or over-ride your sensitivity?

Have you ever thought you should toughen up?

the world within women

Have you ever been ashamed of your sensitivity?

What caused this?

If you were to fully allow and trust your sensitivity, just as it is, what might it want to tell you? ~ In what ways might it be an asset to your life? ~ What is there to value in your sensitivity? ~ How can you give it a more respected and consulted place in your life?

What are the most sensitive times for you in your menstrual cycle? ~ What might they want to bring into your life if your cycle was respected in society and by you?

Remedies and medications – should we use them?

It really is not easy to live in a personal reality that is unacknowledged, disallowed and blindly unsupported in the culture around us. It takes courage and commitment, and a lot of our energy. And, as we have seen, the constant jarring of our inner feminine world against the oblivious masculine ethos that shapes our outer lives costs us and causes us to suffer in our menstruality. Women – especially those who suffer greatly – need and deserve all the support they can get.

Practising conscious menstruality does not mean we shouldn't take remedies or medications if we need them. But the way we go about this is most important. If at all possible, choose practitioners, whether medical or 'alternative', who understand the purposes of menstruality beyond its reproductive function, and are willing to work *with* its mysterious signals rather than *against* them. Ensure that your remedies or medications are supportive of your menstruality situation rather than resistant or suppressive. Always look (hopefully with your practitioner's assistance) to see what might be causing any distress or discomfort you are suffering, rather than just applying a medication that promises to silence its voices by relieving their symptoms.

Remember, as with everything to do with conscious menstruality, **awareness is the** key. With awareness we really can make good choices about what remedial support we might need. Herbalism, naturopathy, and purely energetic methods such as acupuncture, homeopathy and energy healing, in the hands of practitioners who are open to menstruality's own purposes, can be of great assistance. Choose with care, and don't hesitate to ask questions about exactly how the remedies you are offered work. 'Restores hormone balance' is simply not a good enough explanation unless we have already taken our menstruality's advice to check whether it's our hormones, or actually ourself, our environment or the way we are living our life that is out of balance!

> **Remedies WITH awareness**
> allows good self-care
> **Remedies INSTEAD OF awareness**
> perpetuates misunderstanding, fear and resistance, and keeps us deaf to our menstruality's purpose.
> *Choose remedies that* support *your menstruality process, not those that seek to suppress it.*
> *Choose practitioners who understand this*

CHAPTER FOUR

Letting the hidden picture emerge

What will wake us up from the induced coma of resistance to being female? Where can we turn for the knowledge we need to understand ourselves in a whole new way? The answer is as simple, mystical and delightful as a Zen koan[22]. To find something that has been hidden for a long time we need to cease searching in different places with the same eyes, and instead *search in the same place with different eyes*.

For me the discovery of the femenome was very much like learning to 'read' a *Magic Eye* book.[23] There was no text in these books. Popular in the 1990s, each page presented a pattern in which another image was concealed. Beyond offering an intriguing pastime, these fascinating books taught us a new way of looking, to see beyond the apparent and the obvious. In order to discern the hidden image, we had firstly to believe it was in there, for it was completely invisible to our ordinary way of seeing. Only if we could *alter our gaze*, soften our focus, let go of our already-existing perception of what was on the page and *open ourselves to what we did not yet know*, would the three-dimensional depth of the pattern become visible. And from that, as if magically, the hidden image would suddenly emerge so clearly that we would marvel at not having been able to see if before.

---

22   A Zen koan, according to my Concise Oxford Dictionary, is 'a riddle used in Zen to teach the inadequacy of logical reasoning' and that is precisely what we need in the quest for the feminine nature!

23   *Magic Eye III. Visions: A New Dimension in Art. 3D Illusions* by N.E.Thing Enterprises Viking, Penguin Books Australia, 1994

The *feeling* of looking in this way is what we need to adopt if we want to see into the hidden depths of the femenome. It is a simple, humble receptivity: the willingness to stop looking in our usual way and let the truth become *self-evident – let* it *bring itself to us.* When I learned to do my *re-search* in this way, to put aside everything I thought I already knew and allow the femenome itself be my teacher, this is what she revealed herself to be:

The femenome – metacycle of feminine life

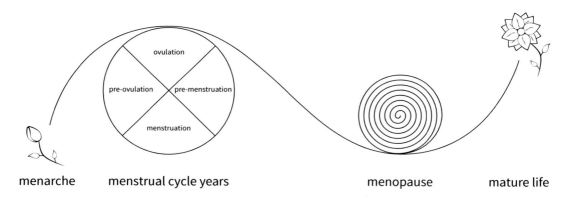

menarche   menstrual cycle years   menopause   mature life

A paradigm revolution

Although throughout the Ages and into our present times we have known the feminine in the threefold archetype of maiden / mother / crone, the femenome design suggests it is now time for us to revise this traditional view. This is in no way a discarding of what has been held sacred for a very long time. But it is, significantly, the turning of a page in evolution, a moving on in consciousness.

> Turning a page in evolution requires a paradigm revolution

This is no small thing to do, for it is this very recognition – that we are not threefold, but fourfold in our archetypal nature – that cracks the code. This is the key that unlocks the door to what has been hidden from our sight for so long. Our feminine body is made to function *in perfect harmonic resonance with the energetic structure of life itself* throughout all of Nature and the universe. We are exquisitely attuned to the very same principles by which Planet Earth, and the whole cosmos around it create and sustain life – principles which are not linear, but cyclical; not static, but rhythmic; not threefold, but fourfold.

> As we dare to go beyond what we have known so far a new panorama of self-understanding opens to us. Reclaiming the lost dimensions of the feminine asks us to move on from the traditional threefold archetype of maiden-mother-crone, and see ourselves as fourfold in nature

As we know, the name menstruality describes the actual workings of the femenome in our daily lives. To understand it more deeply now, we also need to go beyond the notion that our menstrual cycle is all about making babies. While of course it *is* our menstrual cycle that equips us to make babies, and while that *is* a profoundly sacred and precious ability that only women have, creating new lives is actually not the primary, but the *secondary* purpose of our cycle. 'Secondary' does not mean lesser. It means something else comes first, and holds the secondary purpose within it. Over centuries and millennia, the narrowing down of our menstruality's purpose to the reproductive part of its function has played a large part in blinding us to the much bigger role our hormonal sequence intends for us. The *primary* purpose of our menstrual cycle, and indeed of the whole femenome, is not the making of babies, but the making of Self.

> The primary purpose of our menstrual cycle is
> not making babies but making Self

Where the maiden / mother / crone archetype is in danger of holding us back is in its definition of us exclusively in terms of motherhood: before motherhood / motherhood / after motherhood. This model of womanhood fails to recognise the all-important transformational phase between motherhood and cronehood – that of the changing woman, which we traverse during our menopausal years. Without a conscious passage through this vitally self-awakening phase of our development, we are devoid of so much that our hormonal catalysts have in store for us. Similarly, the threefold model would have us move straight from the ovulational phase of our menstrual cycle into our menstrual phase. We all know that is not how it goes – that there is another very distinct stage (pre-menstruation) in between, which generally has some loud and clear messages to bring to us.

Once we have entered the gateway of menarche, the femenome is operating in its all-encompassing way within us every single day until the end of our life. With all four parts in play together its nature is mathematical, musical, medicinal and mystical (another four m's!). Through its mouthpiece, menstruality, the femenome includes the whole flow of energies, changes, moods, dreams, impulses, thoughts and feelings, states of consciousness, developmental imperatives and spiritual invitations that create and accompany the physical 'symptoms' with which we are familiar: premenstrual feelings, periods, hot flushes, emotional variability, etc.

The femenome is our inbuilt design, the energetic circuitry that makes us female. Like roses, like snowflakes, like stars, like fingerprints, each woman's menstruality is unique, soul-tailored and hormonally fine-tuned especially to promote her optimum developmental achievement in her life. The femenome is our teacher-in-residence, our ever-present guide, catalyst, illuminator of every aspect of Self to ourself. Like the most attentive of mothers, it has only our best interests, our highest desires, at heart. It will lead us as the sacred labyrinth does, by a path that is never straight, in a direction that constantly changes, ever inward to the centre of our being.

Life is holographic, or fractal, in form. Its pure structure is replicated in such a way that every particle, even the tiniest, contains exactly the same elements as the whole. As the

Buddhists so wisely teach, the universe is contained in a single grain of sand! In this model no atom is extraneous, no molecule missing. There is no redundancy. When we understand that we are not separate from, but an intimate part of, the world around us, we can look into the Laws of Nature as if they were a mirror – as indeed they are – of every minute detail of our personal, daily experience in the feminine body. Within the great wheel of Nature's seasons, each of our monthly cycles holds about 28 awake-asleep cycles, within which in turn are thousands of breath-cycles, each encompassing a number of heartbeats that are made up of chemical and electrical impulses – all life pulsating, just as the femenome does, in a fourfold pattern that is repeated in endless forms from the minute to the magnum:

opening – open – closing – closed
filling – full – emptying – empty
inward – inner – outward – outer
lightening – light – darkening – dark
expanding – expanded – contracting – contracted

the slow turning of Earth's four seasons, the waxing and waning of the moon, the ebb and flow of tides, the four directions, the four elements, the four phases of plant life, the diurnal rhythms of dawn, daylight, dusk and dark, the rise and fall of breath, our own heart's beat and all the pulsations of biology within us. In a uniquely feminine way, because of our femenome/menstruality patterning, we match them all, and therefore we can find in them an infinite library, a quantum search engine, showing us what we are made of, what we are part of, how we are designed to function.

The femenome's fourfold design

Menarche – the initiate

 The word menarche actually refers to our very first menstruation. But in the overall femenome context it can be used to name the whole stage of a girl's life where she is approaching puberty, experiencing periods for the first time, and then learning to live as a young woman. This will vary from girl to girl, but generally covers a period of several years. Menarche is a threshold, a beginning place, a vulnerable and sensitive step into a whole new realm of our Self.

A girl at this stage is like a bud of the woman she will become. Just as the calyx around a rosebud splits to reveal the colour of the flower inside, menarche brings us glimpses of the woman waiting within the girl to reveal herself, petal by petal.

Menarche is a delicate and tender life-stage, and our girls deserve great care, acknowledgement and guidance as they navigate through its mysterious passage. Initiation is always momentous in nature. There is much to learn, and we are asked to cross a gap between the known and the unknown. Life changes, and we must change with it, even though we do not yet know how to.

Menstrual cycle years – the apprentice[24]

Having crossed the threshold of menarche, we are now entering a phase of the femenome that will probably take us through at least half of our womanly life – forty years or more! Why such a long apprenticeship? Because there is so much to learn and discover in the limitless quest to become our fullest self!

Apprenticeship is on-the-job training – learning by doing. Have you noticed how changeable you are around your month? Our menstrual cycle is designed very cleverly to highlight the four essential aspects of our complex and variable feminine energy spectrum, by presenting them to us one by one as we travel through our cycle phases of pre-ovulation (PO), ovulation (O), pre-menstruation (PM) and menstruation (M) each and every month. The femenome is a very thorough teacher, requiring that we learn by experiencing each part of our fourfold nature separately and repeatedly, ensuring that each is developed

---

24 Penelope Shuttle and Peter Redgrave, in their wonderful book *The Wise Wound*, mentioned earlier, proposed the 'Menstrual Mandala' in the afterword of their revised edition of 1986. I am also deeply indebted to Miranda Gray for her ground-breaking book *Red Moon*, (Element Books, England, 1994). The particular mandala form that I have adopted and adapted is originally hers. I acknowledge that my work rests on the foundation of hers, and develops it further.

the world within women

in balance, and all are included equally. Menstruality's cyclical sequence shows us the contribution each part of our nature can make to our daily life. Our constant journeying through its changes refines and deepens us month by month until we really do know, and can fully embody, our four feminine potentials.

Menopause – the alchemist

Alchemy is the sacred process of energetic transformation. It asks us to deeply understand the separate ingredients of what we wish to transform, so that we can recombine them through an intense progression of distillations and refinements into a higher and truer form. Menopause is a graduation stage in every woman's lifelong development of herself. Now that she has become adept in her four feminine aspects, she no longer needs to experience them singly, but must instead learn to blend and integrate and live them all at once. This is the place in a woman's life where four great currents come together, so it is not surprising that such a powerful process can create some turbulence. Our femenome's hormones are designed to ensure that we do not miss out on the huge gifts of Self they intend for us, and when undertaken consciously, menopause will be a most exhilarating ride.

Mature Life – the manifold self

The femenome's fourth stage, mature life, is often mistakenly thought to be separate from, or beyond, menstruality, but is in fact its *crowning* stage. That is why women at this time of life are known as *crones* – a name we can reclaim with pride. The bud of youth has opened into a many-petalled blossoming – all that was contained in potential inside her can now be radiantly expressed. Because of her menstruality experience she knows all that she is made of and all that she is part of, and now the femenome invites her to balance, refine and integrate every aspect of herself. This is a stage of interior development, a re-attunement toward the soul's consciousness. Its developmental tasks are of a spiritual and expansive nature requiring a depth of self-knowledge and mastery beyond what is possible in younger life.

The holographic femenome: meta-matrix of women

The femenome is the overarching form of the universal feminine – the shape and flow, creativity, intention and momentum of feminine energy throughout the cosmos. Because it is fractal in nature, its patterns and impetus are the same at the macro level as in the micro – the same in its most massive and majestic expression (such as the cycles of planetary orbits) as in its most minute (the breathing of the smallest butterfly). Within this great fractal meta-matrix that shapes every female life, each woman's individual menstruality is a holographic dot, a unique personal replica, the imprint of the universal femenome – part of the whole, yet expressed in her own original way. When we spell holographic as whole-o-graphic we get to see its magic – each individual dot is also a graphic or picture of the whole system, and conversely the whole system is re-mirrored endlessly in the dots that make it up.

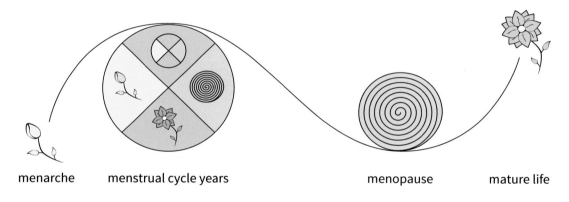

menarche   menstrual cycle years   menopause   mature life

The ingenious four-dimensional design of the femenome is such that it is constantly attuning us to the whole and to specific parts of itself at the same time. In this holographic [whole-o-graphic] way it is a developmental paradigm beyond what our linear minds can fully comprehend. The marvellous layered way in which this works will become clearer for us as we come to know the nature of each phase of our menstruality. But for now, as an example, we can see at a glance how the whole lifelong journey of menstruality (the meta-cycle) is replicated and repeated many times within one part, our menstrual cycle:

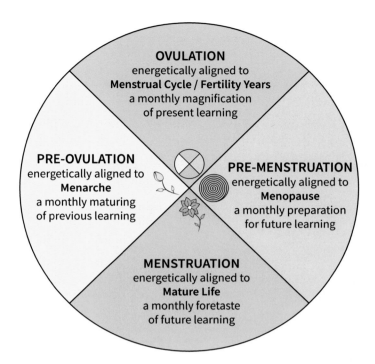

OVULATION
energetically aligned to
Menstrual Cycle / Fertility Years
a monthly magnification
of present learning

PRE-OVULATION
energetically aligned to
Menarche
a monthly maturing
of previous learning

PRE-MENSTRUATION
energetically aligned to
Menopause
a monthly preparation
for future learning

MENSTRUATION
energetically aligned to
Mature Life
a monthly foretaste
of future learning

Our menstrual cycle carries both premonitions and echoes of the four major femenome energies, allowing us foretastes and re-runs of the femenome's big picture at the same time as focussing us on the detail of the current menstruality moment. The femenome is comprehensive, always keeping us in the ever-changing present, but also preparing us for future learning and backing up completed accomplishments as we go. And she is kind. We are never asked to learn our menstruality lessons all at once. They will always be multi-layered, repetitive and (if we can manage not to resist them) gentle.

Conscious menstruality: A cycle-logical approach

There is no logical way to the discovery of these elemental laws.
There is only the way of intuition,

*which is helped by a feeling for the order lying behind the appearance,
and this 'feeling one's way in' is developed by experience.*
Albert Einstein[25]

As a student of psychotherapy I often used to wonder how the **o** got into our word 'psych**o**logical'. Surely, I thought, we are entering into the realm of souls when we do this work, and that **o** should be an **e**. The more I played around with the word *psyche-logical*, the more I liked it. The -logy part of the word refers to its way of knowing – so, *psyche-logy* suggests the soul's way of knowing. And then as I extended my work into menstruality re-search, writing and teaching, I realised how beautifully the word psyche-logical morphs into a new term, unique to our femenome apprenticeship: the cycle-logical approach.

> Conscious menstruality is a cycle-logical way of life

To understand our menstrual cycle, we need to discover its own way of knowing, its own -logy. We need to be intuitively open, as Albert Einstein so eloquently describes it, to *a feeling for the order behind the appearance.* Quite simply this asks us to be willing to learn the cycle's very own logic – to let it be different from our already familiar logic – for if we can accept cycle-logic on its own terms, we can enter a whole new world of femaleness.

> The simple tools of conscious menstruality
>
> No 2
>
> —
>
> *Useful for reclaiming the original meaning of words,
> e.g. cycle-logical = the logic of the cycle*

---

25   Albert Einstein, Preface to Max Planck's *Where is Science Going?* (1933)

> If we can accept cycle-logy on its own terms **we can enter a whole new world of femaleness**

Letting our cycle matter enough…
Getting acquainted through journaling and mendala-making

Getting acquainted with our menstrual cycle is much like working with dreams – the more we take an interest in them, the more they will reveal themselves to us. As with getting a bird to come and sit on your finger, it is important not to go running after this knowledge intellectually, but to let it come to you through experience, gently and gradually, on its own terms.

So the equivalent of holding your finger out for the bird to light on is to make a place for your menstruality awareness to become tangible. The first step is to let your cycle matter enough that it knows you are listening and wanting to hear its messages.

Before reading any further in this book, and if you have not already done so, get yourself a special journal, or make a mendala, so that you can begin recording your cycle on a daily basis. A mendala is a mandala, a circular map of the menstrual cycle, and can look like this:

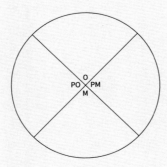

so that as you fill it in with your observations you get to see at a glance the patterns and changes around your month. If you choose to use a mendala, make it big enough to write notes in each day. You don't need to write a lot, but it is important to allow this intimate enquiring and recording on a daily basis.

As for all the exercises in this book, if you do not have a regular or apparent menstrual cycle, you can borrow the moon's cycle to go by, since it is a perfect replica of your inner femininity. For those using that method, your mendala might look like this

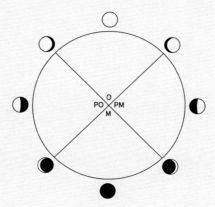

and you will know where you are in it by checking with your moon mirror in the sky each night. And yes, it *is* important that you look to the actual sky moon as your reference, not just a calendar, app or chart. If you want to feel the cadence of your cycle, you will need to open yourself to the energetic presence of the moon, the feelings it stirs in you, not just the idea of it!

~◇~

Make notes in your journal or mendala of your dreams, thoughts, moods, feelings, energies, awarenesses, physical sensations, questions, significant moments, realisations, inclinations and preferences, as they arise in the different phases of your month. You can record these in words, colour, drawings, symbols – whatever is most natural and user-friendly for you.

Let this be something you can enjoy. Be open, curious, interested. Remember, you are on a psyche-logical and cycle-logical quest. This calls for the non-resistant and non-judgemental attitude you have already been practising (see p 42). Let your menstruality begin speaking to you in its own language, without your mind getting too involved in interpreting. Just record and observe, and notice how this feels to you; what patterns begin to emerge; what further insights come as your acquaintance deepens.

The simple tools of conscious menstruality
No 3

mendala

A mendala is a mandala of our menstrual cycle

CHAPTER FIVE

Seeing ourselves in a whole new light

In my work as a menstruality educator I am often touched, and sometimes heart-broken, at how so many women dearly wish to be able to offer their daughters a better preparation for menarche than they received themselves. If your initiation into menstruality was in any way less than what you would wish for yourself, or for a daughter of your own, it will be important to acknowledge this as we go further into learning about our cycle. It will be very healing for the young menarche girl you once were to know that she can be remembered and included now. Embrace her, and bring her with you as you cross the threshold a second time.

a pause to remember...

Invite your inner menarche girl to come sit with you as you are reading this book. Feel her young, vulnerable presence beside you. Open your heart to her story, her experience, and how it made her feel about entering womanhood. Allow yourself to see her as she really was, with all her tenderness and her bright hopes for her life. Take her under your wing. Gather her in to accompany you on this journey now, of reclaiming your true femininity. You may like to

Write her a letter in your journal or special femenome book from your present-day self. Let it be simple and heartfelt

Make a portrait of her, in words, colour, picture or symbol

Write down her feelings

Write down any questions she may have had, even if she did not know then how to ask them. Can you answer these now, or are they still a mystery to you? What would have helped her most, at that age, to receive? To learn? To understand?

What do you want her to know about herself that is really true?

What do you want her to know about being female that is really true?

How would you like her to have experienced her menarche? What did she miss out on that you would like to offer her now (and offer to your daughters or other girls of menarche age)?

Would you be willing to consciously bring this part of yourself into your menstruality quest now, with the intention of healing, supporting, including and offering her anything you may have missed out on when you were young?

Create an offering for your menarche girl from your present self:
it could be a painting, embroidery, montage, poem, dance, garment, song sequence, wall-hanging, declaration, play, drawing, recipe, wrap… using colour, images, textures, words, wishes that speak to the part of her who most needs care, understanding and healing. Take your time, and pour into it all the love and care you would offer a daughter…

Some tips for mothers of daughters

Besides offering the opportunity of healing for what we may have missed out on ourselves as young initiates, the above exercise might be helpful for readers who are themselves mothers of daughters (and also sons) as you decide what menstruality knowledge you want to pass on, and how best to convey it. The time is surely coming when knowledge of the femenome and menstruality will once again be completely integrated into daily awareness in our societies. In the meantime though, the very best thing we can do for our daughters is what you are doing now – filling *ourselves* with the knowledge and lived experience of the feminine nature so we can be torch-bearers for them. We are the generation who are realising we have been dispossessed and our girls deserve more than we had. We can't teach what we don't know. We need to be willing to be the re-searchers for the knowledge we want them to have: to walk the path of re-claiming it for ourselves and for them. If we as mother-figures are not ourselves full of the consciousness our children seek, we will be speaking to them out of our own inner void *and they will feel it.* For now we can only be honest with our young women, and tell them we are currently re-learning ourselves.

Despite our best intentions, there are huge pieces missing from the way we generally present menstruality knowledge to our girls. Firstly, we mostly only teach them (because we were only taught) about one part of their cycle, menstruation, leaving them in the dark about what the femenome is doing inside them all the rest of the month. They need to know that every part is equally important, and brings different gifts – that their cycle makes sense as a whole. And secondly, because we have not completely known the fourfold picture of the femenome we may be at a loss to explain why girls come into their fertility so many years before they are old enough to be mothers. The answer lies in this largely unexplored part of the femenome:

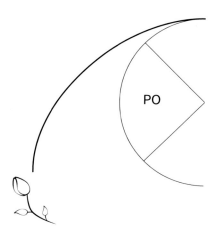

the world within women

and it's all about one of the words we need to reclaim and re-cognise for conscious menstruality. *Virginity* will be discussed later, in the pre-ovulation section. For now, mothers need to be able to reassure daughters that this is the time in a girl's life when her body and sexuality are all her own; when her cycle is not for making babies, but for making Self.

It is very important that girls are allowed to learn about their coming menstruality gradually, little by little, rather than in one download, as many of my generation experienced. (How many of us found a book left discreetly on our bed one night that claimed to tell us everything we needed to know? Or attended a one-off instruction at school and knew that was all we would be getting?). So the more easily, confidently and visibly we who are mothers can live our cycle with all its seasons and changes, the more naturally our daughters will absorb the knowledge and meanings they need. Initiated and familiar from having experienced our cycle alongside us, they will be ready (and hopefully eager) to slip effortlessly into theirs when it arrives.

Although of course the fertility aspect of menstruality is of utmost significance in our womanly lives, it is not the most important part for girls of menarche age to know, and in isolation can be burdensome to a 12 year old. Girls do deserve, though, to know the overall rhythms and resonances of the femenome that they are entering into, and how these relate to the patterns they already know in Nature: the seasons, the coming and going of daylight and darkness, the waxing and waning of the moon, and the rise and fall of breath. They also deserve to know that their energy and feelings will become variable, and that that is okay. They need to know how to make sense of and take care of the changeability they will begin to experience, to know it is purposeful so they will not be distressed by it.

Many mothers would dearly love to celebrate their daughters' menarche with ceremonies or special occasions, and if girls are willing and happy to engage with this, it is a wonderful initiation. We also have to remember though, that while mainstream culture is still largely unaware of and somewhat hostile to menstruality, some young women will feel exposed and uncomfortable if we offer them things their peers are not having. If your daughter wishes to keep her menarche private and low-key, do respect that – however, don't underestimate the influence you can still have simply by being a living model of conscious menstruality yourself. There is plenty of time for our young women to gradually open up to more as they mature and gain confidence. The more you can relax, enjoy and benefit from your cycle in all of the ways described in the following pages, the more your daughter will want of the same experience.

Remember, everything you do for yourself is also for her – so do all you can for yourself!

Reading the femenome mendala

There are two main ways of reading the femenome mendala (the mandala of the menstrual cycle): by observing the many versions of the same fourfold pulse playing out all around us in Nature, and by attuning with a close and respectful attention to our feminine inner world. But whichever way we look, outward or inward, we find the reassurance that the pattern is the same. All we need to do is look *inside ourselves* to feel what we are made of, and *around ourselves* to see what we are part of.

Special note for women with absent or altered menstrual cycles

If you **have had a hysterectomy, but still have your ovaries**, you still have your cycle – though without its most obvious evidence, your monthly periods. So you will be able to recognise where you are in your cycle using your **ovulation** as your compass bearing. To brush up on this very enjoyable method, if you are not already familiar with it from your pre-hysterectomy days, you might like to take a sneak preview now of the tips on p 116 to help you recognise when your ovulation is happening.

If you **do not have ovaries, or if your ovaries are not functioning**, you can get to know the mendala by attuning to any of Nature's helpful reflections, as described below – you may find it easiest to use the moon's monthly cycle, as menstrual cycles are its exact replica within the female body. For you I've included little moon icons in some of the following diagrams to give you a guide to feeling your natural feminine cycle (or you can choose another of the Nature cycles and add your own icons to make any of the diagrams and exercises more relevant and useful for you).

the world within women

> Conscious menstruality is all about learning to live by the
> Laws of Nature – *designed by life to optimise life*

It's not for nothing that we commonly use the terms 'Mother Nature' and 'Mother Earth'. Our planet, after all, is the motherbody in which our lives are conceived, gestated, nourished and sustained, the greatest encyclopaedia of femininity we could possibly consult. We know that our menstrual cycle enables us to become mothers of new lives – the children we may bear. But what we have not been taught to appreciate is how, *because it is made up of the very same ingredients, in the very same sequence, as those of life itself* our cycle is also specifically designed to mother our own lives.

> Our menstrual cycle is specifically designed not only to
> usher in our children's lives **but to mother our own!**

Earth's cycles vary in length, but whether they are annual, monthly, daily or momentary, they are all perfect mirrors of the changes women go through every month. For those of us who for any reason do not experience a physical menstrual cycle, these innumerable holographic mirrors or resonances of Nature around us can be our codex, the reference book we consult to go back to the source. Looking in these mirrors helps us to know where we are, what we can trust, and what is really trying to happen inside us on any particular day of our feminine calendar.

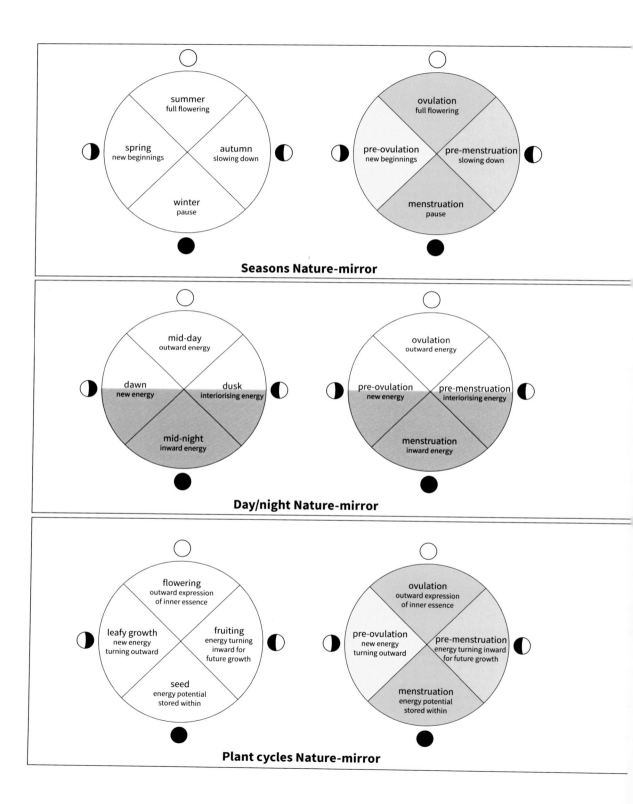

Seasons Nature-mirror

Day/night Nature-mirror

Plant cycles Nature-mirror

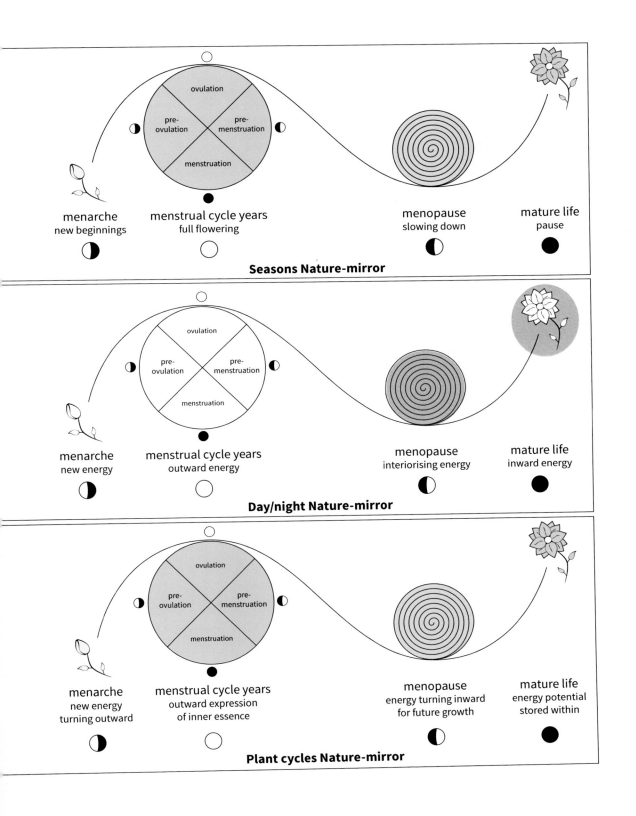

Seasons Nature-mirror

menarche	menstrual cycle years	menopause	mature life
new beginnings	full flowering	slowing down	pause

ovulation
pre-ovulation
pre-menstruation
menstruation

Day/night Nature-mirror

menarche	menstrual cycle years	menopause	mature life
new energy	outward energy	interiorising energy	inward energy

ovulation
pre-ovulation
pre-menstruation
menstruation

Plant cycles Nature-mirror

menarche	menstrual cycle years	menopause	mature life
new energy turning outward	outward expression of inner essence	energy turning inward for future growth	energy potential stored within

ovulation
pre-ovulation
pre-menstruation
menstruation

The moon herself is, of course the quintessential feminine Nature-mirror, and the one for which menstruality, menstruation and menopause are named (mens is from the Latin for month, and moon). Indeed, by an exquisite felicity of the English language we can even quite literally call ourselves moonflowers – moon-flow-ers! We know that the whole moon is always present behind the part that is lit up on any particular night. And that in just the

same way our whole self is always present, even while the femenome illuminates each aspect of us in turn and seemingly separately. When we want to understand how something works, we first take it apart to find out what it is made up of and how each part functions within the whole. That is exactly what is happening under the ever-changing focus of our menstrual cycle.

The Nature-mirrors make sense of ourselves to ourselves. They help us to understand, and therefore be less resistant to, the changes that our hormones bring to us, especially those we have been taught to hold in disfavour. Women who ovulate (those of us not on ovulation-suppressing hormonal contraception, or affected by medical or surgical interventions) generally find that a most enjoyable state, and it is hard not to be disappointed when ovulation's easy and expansive energy begins to contract as we become pre-menstrual. This monthly moment is a poignant echo of the pang of regret that we often feel as summer turns to autumn and we know we must prepare for the season of cold and dark. And yet we also know that, despite being light-fed, plants would not survive if the sun shone on them 24 hours a day, and that our landscapes would quickly become deserts if it were always summer.

As we saw above, the Laws of Nature show us that all living things grow and progress not in a constant or linear fashion, but in fourfold pulsations which are actually alternations, or oscillations, between opposites. There is evidence to show that right from its earliest civilisations, and across all religions and philosophies, humanity has always recognised the number four (and therefore the universal pattern of fourfoldness in life) as representing wholeness, totality, completeness, potency, balance, sacredness and perfection.[26] This

---

26   You can look up The Penguin Dictionary of Symbols, Jean chevalier & Alain Gheerbrant, Penguin, UK, 1996, pp 402-407, if you want to learn more about this fascinating history

the world within women

means that *every* part of our cycle is of equal importance to our development and wellbeing, but also that its purpose can only truly be known *in relation* to the other parts, as an essential contribution to a very finely calibrated and balanced whole.

Our menstrual cycle is all about *inclusion* of every aspect of our nature, and holding them all in perfect balance as we move around our month. Just as a child's spinning top wobbles and falls if it is not well balanced, so our monthly cycle cannot hum along smoothly, as it is designed to do, if any part is missing from the balance. If trees did not shed their leaves in autumn, much as we shed our exuberant and outgoing energy at our premenstrual season, there would not be the exquisite pleasure of new green buds forming a few months later – or that delicious feeling of resurgent energy inside us after our bleeding time is finished. If the tide were always high, we would never get to see the rocks and plants and creatures that live beneath its cover, or smell their pungent smells – likewise, were our premenstrual hormones not to do their work of whipping away our buffer zones of tolerance and overriding, we might never hear the raw but honest voices that speak beneath our usual level of consciousness. A quick check of our seasonal mendala will remind us that if we are menstruating, and in our cycle's winter, we need to be resting and attending to our inner life, as trees and plants do, so our energy can rejuvenate for the coming week. There are many many ways that the Nature-mirrors instruct and support us, and we will explore them in more depth as we study each of our cycle phases in turn.

a pause to reflect…
Nature-mirror meditation using the seasons

Settle comfortably, and breathe in a way that allows you to tune in to the season* that matches where you are in your cycle just now (or where the moon is in her cycle if yours is not apparent to you).

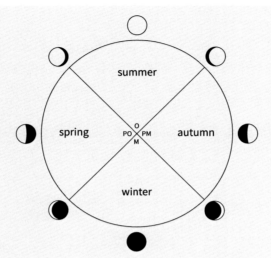

Imagine you are a pupil sitting at the feet of this season, your wise teacher who loves you and all women very dearly. Relax, attend, open your intuition and listen deeply. Let this teacher awaken you, surprise you, inspire you. Let go of any pre-conceived notions, likes or dislikes – be curious and open about whatever might occur to you.

What are the qualities and characteristics of this season?

What are its benefits in the cycle of life?

What feelings do I associate with this season? What words? Colours? Images? Symbols?

What can this season teach me about the current phase of my cycle? About myself? About life and living?

From your learnings make a message for yourself and put it where you can see it. Trust what you have discovered, and let it be a deepening awareness each time you come again to this cycle point over the next few months.

~◇~

*you can, of course, do this same meditation with any of the Nature-mirrors, e.g. tides, plant cycles, directions, elements, day/night cycles, breath cycle – whatever appeals most to you

Personal energy mendalas
looking inside us to see how we make sense

It can't be denied that culture has to a large extent succeeded in suppressing the feminine consciousness. But fortunately for us it has not yet managed (though scientific efforts are afoot and rapidly gaining ground) to eliminate entirely the compelling prompts of menstruality that speak and sometimes even shout from inside every woman's body. We may have forgotten how to read them, but the femenome has not forgotten how to transmit!!

> We may have forgotten how to receive the femenome's signals **but she has not forgotten how to transmit!!**

It can be challenging to learn to trust her voices, comprehend her language and discern her messages to us, for they are deeply unpopular in our times. Moreover, as we have seen, they are 'hidden in plain sight', as the legendary Holy Grail was, in the very last place we would think to look for wisdom – right in the most disparaged parts of our long-disparaged menstruality.

Fenomenology
A lifelong doctorate in the univers-ity of the femenome

If we want to know how something works we need to study it on its own terms. Scientists wishing to understand everything there is to know about a plant or animal will go and find that organism in its own habitat – the context in which everything about it makes sense. Serious moonflower-hunters need to follow their nose at night. In psychotherapy school I was taught a method called the phenomenological approach, which has greatly helped me to *learn from the femenome itself* instead of mistaking what culture says about it for knowledge. According to phenomenology we simply observe the thing we are studying with an open mind. We let it show us *by being itself* what it is, what it does, what its meanings might be – without any previous assumptions getting in the way. We want to know what the logic and language of that phenomenon is in its own nature, and for its own purposes.

As we have already discovered, when we want to talk and think and feel about our feminine reality in a whole new way, we need words that have not existed before. So it makes sense to feminise and specialise the words phenomena and phenomenology to make them specific to our study. If we call the phenomena of menstruality *fenomena,* then conscious menstruality becomes a *fenomena-logical approach – learning to trust and live by the unique and inherent logic of the workings of the femenome inside us.*

> **A fenomena-logical approach** asks us to trust and live by **the logic of the fenomena**: the workings of the femenome inside us

The name fenomenology gives our quest the status it deserves – a subject of study in its own right, with its own curriculum. And it allows us to have the conversations we need to have with each other, for in the University of the Femenome, we are our own learning resource, our own database, our own textbooks, and our own fieldwork. Because it is all about consciousness, there are no limits to how deep we can go in fenomenology – it is studied by experience, and is quite literally a subject designed to take (at least) a whole lifetime to fully comprehend.

> **Fenomena** are the things that happen inside us because of our menarche, menstrual cycle, menopause and mature life

Fenomena are simply the things that happen in our menstruality – often the very things we complain about and take remedies for – such as monthly bleeding, mood changes, strong emotions, energy fluctuations, period pain, and in menopause, hot flushes, sleep disturbances, memory-failure, and many more: undeniably a quirky and fascinating array. Some fenomena are really fun, like the sexy and confident feelings we get at ovulation. Or funny, like the word-scrambles some women experience in menopause. Each stage of the femenome has its own

the world within women

fenomena for us to encounter and learn from, and every woman will experience a different blend of them, custom-built to her soul's own developmental requirements for her.

Curious as it may seem, the fenomena of menstruality are not just impediments to our lives and relationships that should be ignored if they can't be eliminated, but the tools, or teaching aids, or clever devices by which the femenome forms and shapes us throughout our lives. They are the energetic prompts, the wake-up calls, the means by which she endeavours to get our attention so that we don't miss out on the gifts of development and consciousness she wants to bring to us.

Remember, our menstrual cycle years are the apprenticeship stage of our lifelong menstruality. We are in training, or formation, for all those years under the femenome's tutelage. What she has to teach us cannot be learned in the current conditions in our world, where the feminine has long been discredited. It can only be rediscovered from the inside of ourselves – from the original blueprint stored in our hormonal archives. So it is inevitable that the femenome's training school will feel counter, or alien, to others we have known.

Our menstrual cycle spins us so we can be worked, formed and refined as we turn, like the raw material a woodworker or metal-worker places in a lathe. The femenome is the lathe, and her fenomena, like the worker's tools, are held against our rotating Self to shape us into all that we can be. Or we might feel our cycle as a spinning potter's wheel with our Self the clay at its centre, and the femenome the artist. There we turn between her shaping hands, feeling their intent and loving and sometimes provocative pressure on us as she forms and forms and forms us to the potential she knows is in us.

> Living by menstruality's counter-culture fenomena takes **fenomenal courage** and forges in us the reward of **fenomenal wisdom**

We will learn much more about the way the fenomena shape us and bring us to consciousness as we study each phase of our cycle in more depth. For now let's consider a couple of examples of applied fenomenology to see how fenomena that have seemed to disable us or undermine our trust in our cycle can be re-cognised in a much more redeeming light than is usually allowed them.

Being irrational

How often have you been accused (by another or yourself) of being 'irrational' at particular times in your cycle, notably, for most women, when we are pre-menstrual or menstrual. And it is true – we really can feel, think and behave completely differently at the various times in our month, much to the bafflement of ourselves and others around us. It can feel as if our hormones have fried the wiring in our brains, making it completely impossible for us to remain logical, reasonable or tolerant, even if we were all of those things only yesterday! Why is it that something that was a slight irritation one week can feel like grounds for divorce the next, according to our hormonal state?

Before we decide that there is absolutely no basis for our apparently irrational changes of mood and tolerance levels, or that our hormones need medicating or regulating, let's take a closer look at that word 'irrational'. If we are looking at it through a conscious menstruality lens we will remember to apply one of our simple tools (-), and see it like this:

ir - rational

and furthermore, we will remember to look without judgement or pre-existing notions. With the hyphen we can easily see that this word does not mean anything bad or invalid. It very simply means not-rational, or other-than-rational. Now we apply another of our simple tools (?) and become curious in an in-nocent way. If our menstruality state is not rational, it must be something else, so what is it? We may then remember that it has only been in the last few hundred years of patriarchal dominance that rationality has been valued above all our other faculties, as the only one deserving to be taken seriously. But of course the femenome is not confined to male standards of validity. She does not prize any one faculty over another but holds them all equally in balance within the monthly cycle. Thus it becomes evident that the famously ir-rational parts of our cycle are those in which we are simply in one of our other faculties! Why use only one (rationality), when we have four?

In this way, if we can pluck up our fenomenal courage, the seeming handicap of ir-rationality at certain times in our cycle becomes converted into one of our greatest female assets. A most profound developmental advantage of our menstrual cycle is that it will take us, whether we like it or not, through each of our four faculties in sequence every month, so that we cannot become overly reliant on rationality, but *are compelled to* allow the other three to have input into our lives on a regular basis. It is not that we experience any one of them in isolation at its favoured time of the month, but more as if the spinning axis of our cycle brings us (as long as we are not resisting) to bask in the optimal light of each in turn. This allows us, if we care to use it, the richness and resourcefulness of a fourfold perspective on anything and everything – a fourfold approach to comprehending, processing and resolving every issue life may present, and an understanding that is more precise and yet at the same time more complex and multi-faceted than rationality can ever be.

> Being ir-rational asks for **conscious engagement** in one of our other faculties

In mendala form, for most women, our monthly faculty map looks something like this:

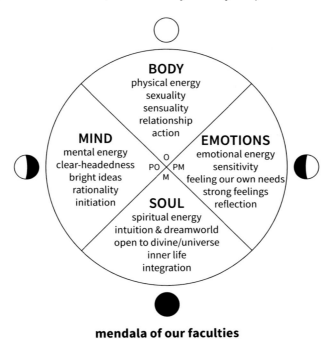

mendala of our faculties

allowing us to see at a glance how vast the potentials of being ir-rational are. In fact, for three quarters of every month women are naturally in states where faculties other than rationality are predominating, affording us the fenomenal wisdom to sense, intuit, experience, create, love and respond to life at far greater depths and with much more energetic scope than rationality alone could ever provide.

So now we can see that our much-scorned hormonal irrationality is actually a very in-our-face invitation from the femenome to open to a deeper capacity in our feminine nature than we have been allowed to trust or develop in our highly adapted lives. When we are aware of our cycle as an apprenticeship, and allowing of its training in using our other three faculties much more consciously and confidently, *we can even begin to experience our ir-rational moments as beyond-rational* – but this involves some careful preparation and practice. To really go beyond-rational asks for a deep and very complete surrender, and for this we fortunately have our hormones to assist us so that we do not unwittingly remain in a limited mental version of our ir-rational faculties.

> In conscious menstruality when our hormones seem to make us **irrational** they are really inviting us to go **beyond-rational**

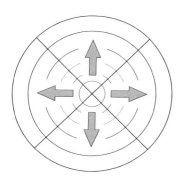

The spinning of our menstrual cycle creates a centrifugal impetus for our growth, expanding our Self capacity outward in an ever-widening circumference like ripples on a pond spreading evenly across the whole spectrum of our being, both rational and ir-rational.

As we have noted before, and will rediscover again and again, it is not for nothing that our menstrual cycle apprenticeship takes about half our life to complete – its lessons are profound, and really do require the constant repetitions of the hundreds of cycles we go through. These learnings are not accessible by the mind alone – they are often subtle and mysterious, and rationality is just not enough. Our apprenticeship takes place in our body, in our relationships with the world, in the deep resonating chambers of intuition, and in openness to realms beyond the scope of mere intellect. There is infinitely much to learn, for in submitting to the femenome we open our consciousness to the boundless yet intricate workings of the universe itself. Menstruality lessons are lived, felt, breathed, discerned, revealed – whispered by the stars, or by a single flower opening and closing. They are gently and gradually realised. They cannot be hurried, as the great, slow orbits of the planets cannot be hurried.

The femenome's apprenticeship is long because it is **magni-ficent**. It is our menstruality hormones' job to **magnify** details in our lives, make them bigger so that we *have to* notice them and let them in to our awareness. So that we realise these apparently small things *do* matter greatly. Have you noticed how the really significant and most life-changing shifts in our personal development are often achieved in a seemingly tiny decision or momentary realisation?

> The femenome's apprenticeship is long because it is **magni-ficent**. Femenome hormones **magnify the minutiae** of our lives to bring them under the spotlight of consciousness

a pause to consider…

Learning to engage fully with our cycle's ir-rational phases is a deep and delicate art which needs to develop gradually over time. A good starting place is to begin noting on your mendala or in your journal when in your cycle you feel clearest in your mind; when you most enjoy your body and its sensations; when you tend to experience life through a heightened emotional lens; and when you feel most drawn to and at ease in your spirituality, intuition or dream world.

What are the responses, thoughts and feelings that give you clues? Record these over several months, so that you can see what pattern emerges. This will become very important to know, as you begin to want to plan your life according to your cycle.

Remember, we are not exclusively in any one faculty at any one time, and life as we know it will keep pulling us back into our mind wherever we are in our cycle. For now just notice when in your month each way of being feels more natural, most intense, or seems to function best.

Being changeable

Directly related to our ir-rational abilities, another of the menstrual cycle fenomena that often meets with criticism from ourselves and others is our feminine changeability. It is true that we women are variable by nature, and when measured against the masculine standard of constancy, we are inevitably seen to fall short. But what if we don't measure ourselves against that seemingly objective, but actually highly misleading standard? What might we see in our changeability if we take the judgement out of our eyes?

Do we ever stop to consider what it takes for us women to create a cohesive and coherent life out of an internal world that is in constant flux? Our cycle is forever expanding and contracting everything inside us – our confidence, our energy, our sociability, our mental clarity, our emotional intensity and sexual inclinations. Like the yo-yos we played with in childhood, the momentum of our lives is made up of constant movement in one direction, then the other. Thankfully we have the Nature-mirrors to reflect to us that this is actually how life works! But how **do** we keep it all together?

Once again our simple little conscious menstruality tool (–) lets us see at a glance that the feminine **change-ability** we all possess is truly something to be acknowledged and admired. Because of the pressures on us throughout history to be more like men if we want to be included and taken seriously, we have overlooked this fenomenon that really deserves our attention. If we can be allowed to develop it and use it consciously we will find we have much to contribute *because of* our unique ability to weave the strands of our fourfold energies into a variable but self-stabilising life.

the world within women

> Feminine change-ability is our fenomenal ability to weave the strands of our fourfold energies into a variable yet coherent and self-balancing life

We live in times where this capacity is much needed in our world – where resistance to difference leads to fear of otherness and even to the bizarre and outrageous extreme of war with our fellow humans. Women are naturally reconciling differences inside themselves from week to week every month. Although we may not be fully conscious of it, we are already experts in getting opposite elements to come together harmoniously because our own nature demands it of us. Precisely *because of* our Nature-matching, ever-changeable hormonal rhythms, we women literally embody a profound extra dimension of harmony. We should not ignore or undervalue that! The more we wake up to our change-ability, stop trying to deny and hide it, and consciously become adept in handling its challenges, the more we can make it work around us in our communities and cultures as well.

Just as the whole of the moon is always present, even while only parts of it are visible to us, so our whole self is always present too. Our change-ability does not cut us off from any aspect of ourself, as long as we stay aware of its purpose in constantly moving the spotlight from one to another. So the more we learn to trust our changes and move gracefully in accordance with them the better we can hula-hoop our way through our months, taking every perspective into account as we go. Just imagine a world where women's vari-ability, in contrast to and in balance with men's stability, will become sought after and prized for the extra dimensions of sophistication and complexity it can add to political deliberations and decisions! To create that world we need to prepare first by becoming accomplished adepts of change-ability in our own personal lives and relationships…

a pause to reflect…

Next time I notice myself being changeable because of my cycle, how shall I respond? (If you have a disrupted or absent cycle for medical or other reasons, you can do this exercise for any kind of changeability or contradiction you notice in your life). Can I give myself permission to slow down, breathe myself calm, and open to the messages in **all** aspects of my feelings, even if they are different this week from last week? What if I am being shown that the truth is multi-faceted? That even if parts of me appear contradictory at different times of the month, they all have something to contribute to my understanding?

See if you can begin a practice of recording on your mendala or in your journal feelings, thoughts and responses, just as they are at various moments in your cycle, even if they appear contradictory. Write, draw or symbolise them for each week or day of your month.

without judgement

without editing them, even subtly

and without trying to work out which time-of-the-month voice is truer, or more acceptable to you

It may take a little time before you can really look at the trickier ones with a calm, unjudging and curious eye, and begin accepting what is true about them, even if they present in harsh or distressed ways at certain cycle phases. If this is difficult for you, know that you are not alone. Some of the exercises in the pre-menstrual section later in this book may help you to find ways of working with the places where you (and many of us) get stuck.

PART THREE

Revealing

the femenome's cycle-logical matrix

CHAPTER SIX

Light side of the moon: bringing consciousness to our outer life

*The femenome is a loom
upon which we weave throughout our lives
the fabric of our own Self.
The more conscious we are of our colours
the richer will be the pattern.*

As we go into more detail now of what the femenome is made up of, let's remember again that although we all carry its powerful imprint inside us we are each born with our own unique version of it. This book is not in any way suggesting you should conform to the model presented here, but invites you to use it as an aid to discerning your own overall pattern and the monthly variations within that.

> The femenome is present in all of us yet unique to each of us

The descriptions that follow are only the briefest of notes, introductory sketches of energies that are boundless in depth and scope. A small handbook such as this cannot hope to do any more than attract your attention to what is inside you, waiting to reveal itself to you month by month, over years and decades. Perhaps it can serve as a prospectus for the lifelong learning to be gained in the School of the Femenome. The actual curriculum can only be accessed by daily attendance.

Special note about mendalas

Although the mendalas you will see in this book are drawn in four equal quarters, of course no woman's cycle is so precisely or regularly divided. So it's important to know that the mendala represents *energetic* differentiations rather than mathematically or proportionally correct divisions. The number of days you spend in each phase can vary according to who you are or what is currently happening in your life. Don't try to make your cycle conform to a nice, tidy mendala with straight lines in it. Have fun devising ways of incorporating all its variability into your own mendala-making.

Light side of the moon: bringing consciousness to our outer life

Medicine has taught us to count our cycle using the onset of our period as day 1, and you may prefer to continue with this custom. However, although this view has a certain convenience (or, dare we say it, rationality) in that it is easy to recognise, it can also be seen as contradictory to the energetic shape of our month, and a further distraction from the connection we all need to *feel* to the rise and fall of our feminine rhythm. The first day of bleeding is for many women a releasing or relieving of energy, but it carries the feeling of ending an old cycle, not beginning a new one.

So, to find our beginning place we will return to the source. What is it that powers the spinning of the femenome's lathe, her potter's wheel, our menstrual cycle? It is light.

> The hand of the femenome constantly spinning our cycle is light

The relationship of menstrual cycles with the moon is not just folklore, or a pretty metaphor. It is very real. The marvel of how we are made is that the pineal gland which governs our menstruality hormones – despite being positioned 'way down deep in the centre of our head, tucked in between the hemispheres of our brain, in behind the spot between our eyebrows – is ultra-sensitive to light. In the original design of things it is the light nights of the full moon that causes women to ovulate. In our 'advanced' technological lifestyles though, we have electricity to make all our nights equally light, so our bodies have lost their natural ovulation signal. However, if we once again lived in our female element, the natural rhythm of lighter and darker nights caused by the waxing and waning of the moon would cause us all to ovulate at the full moon and menstruate at the dark of the moon.

Light is the original and primary energy source of life itself. In the biblical account God says 'let there be light' as the very first step, the tinder strike, of creation. The monthly moment when the femenome says 'let there be light' is the first appearance of the new moon, the thinnest crescent, in our western skies. That is a good reason for us to feel the cessation of our bleeding as the beginning of a new cycle. (Although technically the middle of menstruation is our turning point, pre-ovulation is the first whole phase of each new cycle).

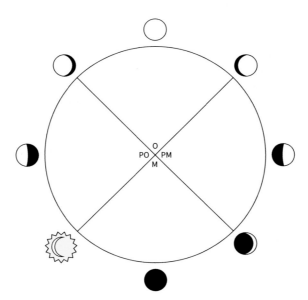

And to make further sense of this re-cognition (new way of understanding), our cycle's pre-ovulation phase also corresponds whole-o-graphically with the first of our lifelong femenome stages, menarche.

Pre-ovulation in the holographic femenome

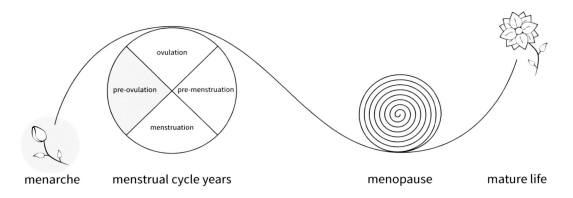

menarche menstrual cycle years menopause mature life

Fenomenology 201: Pre-ovulation

Energy of initiation

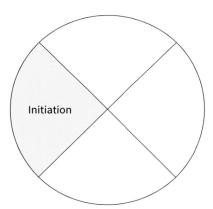

Very often in my conscious menstruality workshops, when I ask women to describe their experiences of each mendala quadrant, they find they have little or nothing to say about pre-ovulation. Sometimes it even remains blank on the whiteboard, because, as the women say, they 'just feel normal'. And it is probably true, in our rationality-worshipping cultures, that this is the time of our month where we fit most easily into the way of functioning that is expected of us. Pre-ovulation is the phase where our mind is at its best, a time of clear thinking, ability to plan and organise, and the relief of knowing we *can* be rational and logical after all. Life becomes easy, and the pace picks up effortlessly.

Nevertheless, it is well worth getting to know the particular energies we do experience at this time of our month. They are usually easy and enjoyable for women, and what they have to contribute to our fourfold monthly experience is just as important and beneficial to our development as any other phase.

Nature-mirrors at pre-ovulation

What a joyous thing it is to step out into a fresh new morning. Everything is awakening, quickening, brightening, opening. Birds are singing, the light is soft and clear, there is a sense of refreshment, hope and potential. Our attention is naturally aroused and attuned forward, in anticipation of what may become possible in this new day.

We know – and it is sometimes poignant knowledge – that in this world nothing lasts or is permanent. Everything changes, comes and goes. But the blessing on the flipside of that truth is that everything goes and comes – life is also full of renewals and beginnings. Goodbyes make way for hellos. Morning ushers light out of darkness, sound out of silence, movement out of stillness. In springtime the stirring and awakening we love to feel is magnified all around us. There is a sense of burgeoning, of increase and hope in every living thing, in the weather, and even in the air itself. Twigs fatten with new leaves and all manner of eager green growth thrusts up and out into the light from its dormancy in the soil's darkness. What has been tightly held in bud unfurls. All that has been frozen and still thaws and moves. Colour appears out of bleakness. And in the irresistible stimulus of increasing light, plants and animals produce new lives. We can see the same dynamic endlessly repeated in myriad forms around us. A tide that has receded in seeming farewell pauses and begins to return. The moon that had completely disappeared, last seen as a fragile crescent hanging high in the eastern morning, mysteriously reappears in its own mirror image 4 days later, low in the western sky at evening.

In harmony with all these Nature-mirrors, our pre-ovulational energy is all about renewal, emergence, increase, awakening and quickening. The direction of movement in our consciousness and energy is from inward to outward; from empty to full; from beneath to above; from closed to open; from contemplative to active. Like all Nature cycles, our menstrual cycle has two opposite phases that are stable (ovulation and menstruation), and two that are transitional (pre-ovulation and pre-menstruation) where the energetic flow moves between the stable poles. Pre-ovulation is a dynamic time, an energetic initiator, enjoyable in the same way as morning and spring are enjoyable. We might feel like a bird soaring upward into the sky after the heavy, withdrawn time of our bleeding. Or a leaf unfurling to the sun's warmth – a shoot springing up out of the ground. We feel ourself unfolding, our energy rising like sap in a tree.

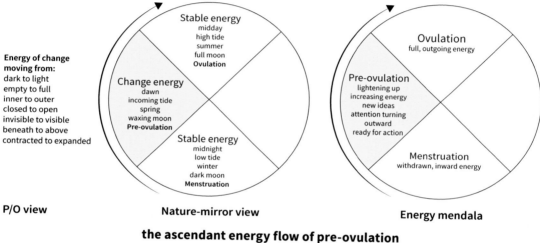

the ascendant energy flow of pre-ovulation

There are also fourfold Nature-mirrors that are not cyclical, but still part of the universal holograph we are attuned to through the femenome. These include **the four directions**, and **the four elements**. By now you will easily recognise that **east** is the **direction** relating to our cycle's pre-ovulation phase. East is where we look to, with hope, anticipation, expectation of sunrise; for reassurance that fresh starts and new beginnings are always possible; for a sense of refreshment, rebirth and rejuvenation.

The **element** that matches pre-ovulation, being light, free, quick, moving, refreshing, clear, awakening and revitalising, is **air**. Air, like our pre-ovulational self, loves to be unhindered, penetrating and far-reaching. It is the first and most essential thing a newborn

the world within women

life needs for survival. Air makes us alert, helps us to be active. It wakes things up, and keeps them going.

Perhaps the simplest and most immediately accessible Nature-rhythm of all (although we can be surprisingly unconscious of it) is right inside us, in the constantly rising and falling cadence of our own breath. Any time we want to heighten our awareness of a particular menstrual cycle moment, we can find its sensory replica in our breath cycle. This can be a simple but most enriching meditation for those wishing to engage very fully in the consciousness potentials of the femenome.

a pause to experience…
Breath meditation for pre-ovulation

Find yourself a place where you can be very comfortable. At this time of the month you may prefer to be outside in the fresh air. If possible face east and allow your heart to be open to the blessings that come from that direction. Feel the anticipatory and redeeming nature of them, and allow yourself to receive their reassurance, no matter your current circumstances or frame of mind.

Begin to focus on your breath, allowing it to settle into a pace and rhythm that are easy for you. Next, take a deeper breath ~ really stretching your ribs open ~ hold the air in your lungs briefly ~ then breathe out fully through your mouth. Repeat this in an unhurried way a few more times until you feel you have cleared out any old energy from your body and can open to some truly fresh new breaths. Once again, let your breathing settle into a relaxed pace and rhythm.

Now start to allow a slight pause after your out-breath, to feel the sensation of emptiness and the desire that starts there for your next in-breath. As you take that in-breath notice the sweet sensation of receiving after not-receiving. Of renewal. Of refreshment. What is that like for you to allow? Feel your ribs expanding and your lungs filling. Be generous, as air itself is generous. Fill up. Feel as consciously as you can what breath wants to do for you when you let yourself have it. Enjoy what comes to you. Notice the effect this creates in your overall state of energy. You may become aware of a heightened state of pleasure, alertness, expectancy, preparedness – a waking-up feeling. You may feel your head wanting to lift, your eyes to open and look outward, a sense of expansion and readiness inside.

This is pre-ovulational energy. Yours to enjoy. Relax into it and let it nourish you. Take as much time, and as many times as you wish to get acquainted with it on very intimate terms. Let it become a conscious part of your way of life, a resource to draw from. Enjoy it to the full each month as you traverse your pre-ovulation phase. And anytime at all, when you need a sense of renewal, find it in your in-breath.

Another rich resource we can draw from in enjoying and celebrating our menstrual cycle is its felicitous fit with the seasonal festivals within the Celtic tradition. The Celts preserved a Nature-based sense of the year's cycle, and as a refinement of the laws of fourfoldness they marked **the four cross-quarterly seasonal turning points** as well as the four cardinal points of summer and winter solstices and spring and autumn equinoxes. These additional festivals fall at the changeover times in our monthly cycle, so they are worth knowing to add to our enjoyment of the interplay between our internal monthly seasons and those of the turning year around us. (The dates given in this book are opposite to the traditional Celtic ones, to fit the southern hemisphere seasons.)

Seasonal festival Nature-mirror for pre-ovulation (southern hemisphere)

the world within women

Personal energy mendala at pre-ovulation

The shift we feel happening inside us as we finish our period and move into the next phase is generally a happy one for us. As in clearing weather, we feel things become lighter, brighter, sharper and more focussed.

Pre-ovulation, as the Nature-mirrors show us, is the time when our energy and attention are turning from inward preoccupations to a more outer focus. We know when we are entering our personal monthly spring, for just as our menarche held all the energy of ourself in bud, so each of our monthly pre-ovulation seasons will bring us that same feeling of our own swelling potential. Not only will our physical energy pick up, but our **mind** will quicken. Women at this point of the cycle generally find that their spirits lift naturally, their mood lightens and their capacity for activity and achievement increases. Like plants emerging from the soil and sprouting their new leaves we feel a renewed interest in the world around us, and how we can find our place and make things happen in it. We want to express ourselves, participate and contribute our gifts.

Pre-ovulation highlights the faculty of **MIND**

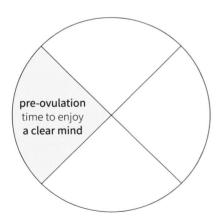

pre-ovulation
time to enjoy
a clear mind

A knowledge of the whole mendala can help us appreciate more fully the wonderful asset that our mind is to us, not as superior to, but *in relationship with* our other faculties. Remembering that pre-ovulation is our phase of *transitioning* from the deeply inner world of menstruation to the expansively outer world of ovulation, we can see that our mind is like an executive officer. Its job is to be practical, to make energy into ideas that can then be expressed as actions. Our pre-ovulational energy wants to bring what is inside us out into forms that can be seen, heard and felt in the world, our love made manifest and shared with others.

We know how conception works – that it is in the coming-together of opposites that the spark of new life is struck. Our menstrual cycle design holds the elements of our nature separately, and in oppositional balance, so that in the spaces between there is a constant interplay of Self creating itself. At this time of the month we are not yet in the place of conceiving other lives. Our conceptions are of Self and for Self. There is a very special and exquisite Nature-mirror of this particular grace in our pre-ovulation state (which of course we have first encountered at menarche). Have you noticed how sometimes, when conditions are just right, you can see in the embrace of the new moon's bright crescent the soft silhouette of the whole moon? The new moon is pregnant with herself, with her own light. And so are we at this time of our month. In its dynamic role between the soul and body realms within us, pre-ovulation is the phase of ignition, invigoration, initiation, innovation, illumination and, in more ways than one, inspiration. We are beautifully full of our own potential.

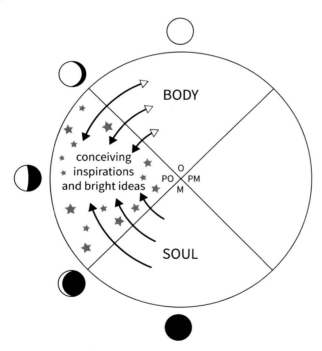

pre-ovulation: expressing soul in ideas and actions

the world within women

In terms of how conscious we want our lives to be, these things matter greatly. Inspiration is another name for our in-breath, the breath-cycle match for pre-ovulation. In older times, the word for air was 'spirit'. So, to draw a breath was (and still is, surely) quite literally to take into oneself bodily, spirit, the divine. Poets and artists speak of 'the muse', a traditionally female spirit of inspiration who opens the way for communications from divine sources, or mediates between this world and the Other. Like the women of old, returning from their menstrual retreats to bring messages from the gods back to their community, our task is to bring up and out into the world the realisations, dreams, creative visions and intuitions we have received from our soul or unconscious during our menstruation.

The femenome, through conscious menstruality, teaches us to be our own muse, receptive to inspirations from the spiritual realms beyond us and those within us. In keeping our pre-ovulational channels open and clear we allow our spiritual consciousness to flow upward and outward into actions and expressions in our physical lives. We truly can – we are designed to – create heaven on earth!

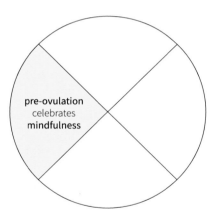

Special features of the pre-ovulation phase

As we learn to let the femenome be our teacher all around the month, we will begin to notice that each phase of our menstrual cycle brings its own extra tutorials (or special apps!) to assist us in living to the fullest. Many of these will be very specific to our own personal developmental journey, and they will vary according to our needs at particular times. However, some are so universally applicable that I will describe them here, so that you can get a taste of how conscious menstruality works – and also so that you can be on the lookout for further lessons your own personal femenome might wish to bring to you.

Fresh starts and new beginnings

Simple as it is, the reminder pre-ovulation brings to us each and every month that

> we can always make a fresh start, no matter what

is deeply consoling. When we feel stuck, over-whelmed, exhausted or despondent, it is so reassuring to remember all of the ways Nature tells us that new beginnings are a regular and reliable fact of life – the sun will rise again in the morning; the tide will come flowing back in from its withdrawal; spring will follow even the harshest winter, and a new in-breath will surely follow the one we just sighed out.

Knowing there is a phase in our month where fresh starts will come naturally and easily can help us trust the letting-go process, and even the times when we simply don't know what to do or how to find the answers we need. This is much more important and empowering than it may seem at first glance. If we are not taking notice of where we are in our cycle at times of low energy or emotional struggle we can easily put pressure on ourselves to solve problems, find solutions or push through obstacles. Unfortunately, despite our best intentions, using this familiar method generally results in our resorting to what we already know, wearing ourselves out by trying harder and harder to make things work in old ways. As our experience of conscious menstruality grows, we learn to trust that our next pre-ovulation phase is coming, and our energy and clarity will naturally rise again from a fresh source inside us, bringing us new insights and options we couldn't see before.

> Pre-ovulation's reminder that life will always bring us the chance to begin anew helps us learn the precious art of self-forgiveness

the world within women

Remembering this wise lesson of our pre-ovulation phase can also help us develop the valuable art of self-forgiveness. We all occasionally experience times of regret, or even remorse. Sometimes we lose hope, or feel heart-crushing grief. There are moments when our best endeavours are not enough, we make mistakes, or cannot bring about the outcomes we want. It is so vitally important at times such as these that we can locate within ourselves the place where we know for sure (because we have experienced it month after month) that life will never deny us the chance to begin anew. So many times in my own life when sorrow, grief or a sense of failure have threatened to break my heart, I have whispered the 'no matter what' part of pre-ovulation's lesson to myself, and felt it soften the bruising grip of self-blame or despair inside my chest. It is only from this gentle and open place that we can hope to access anything that will help us take our next step, or even our next breath.

   As we traverse the decades of our menstrual cycle years we will discover more and more deeply the many guises this (and every other) lesson of the femenome can take in our life experience, bringing us endless gifts, from the hope-renewing to the life-saving.

a pause to reflect...
Invitations of pre-ovulation: hope, trust and renewal

What is there in my life that would benefit from a fresh start?

Do I easily give myself permission to let go and begin anew, or do I struggle with that?

What are my fears around it? What could I trust more if I let my cycle teach me?

What inside me is asking for renewal, refreshment, inspiration?

How can I open to this energy more fully: in my pre-ovulation time? All the time?

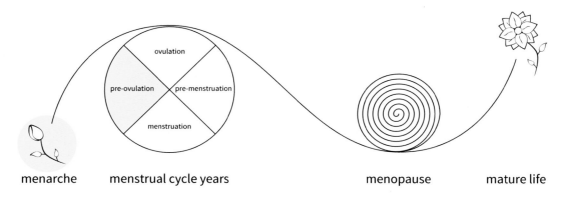

menarche   menstrual cycle years   menopause   mature life

Remembering that pre-ovulation is the part of our cycle that matches menarche in the holograph of the femenome, we will be looking for the ways in which it amplifies and matures the learnings and energies we experienced as very young women just entering our menstruality – especially that mysterious virginity curve between menarche and our menstrual cycle years.

We have already noted (p 73) that there is a need for us, as students of the femenome, to look with fresh eyes at the place of virginity in our womanhood. As with so much in the fate of the feminine over the last few thousand years, virginity is something whose true meaning has been lost to us, leaving us only a remnant that does not serve us well. We are admonished, especially at menarche, not to *lose* our virginity, but we are never taught how to *find it* in the first place!

> We grow up being told not to **lose** our virginity but we are never taught how to **find** it in the first place! Virginity, in its original meaning, is all about self-ownership

The word virginity means much more than our current understanding of never having had sex. What is of crucial importance to us as practitioners of conscious menstruality is to reclaim its original meaning – a virgin is someone who, regardless of her sexual choices, *belongs to herself, and not another.* We have splendid role models in some of the virgin goddesses of old – Diana, Aphrodite (Venus in the Roman version), Athene, Artemis. They had their lovers, but did not give over their sovereignty or authority to them. They remained self-possessed, rather than allowing themselves to be the possession of any man or god[27]. What is more, contrary to current popular belief, virginity in its true sense *is renewable.* The Greek goddess of marriage, Hera, ritually celebrated the renewal of her virginity every spring by bathing in a special pool, mirroring the renewal of virginal youth and fertility our beautiful feminine Planet Earth also undergoes each spring. Virginity is the state of self-renewal, freshness and new beginnings that we very naturally return to each month at the end of our period. It is a very beautiful energy, clear and light and full of eagerness to learn and grow, to seek adventure, freedom and true self-reliance. What I love to say to the women on my conscious menstruality courses, is

> Have all the sex you want **but don't lose your virginity!**

Menarche virginity is a very important time in the development of Self, a time when our femininity and sexuality are *for ourself alone.* At this tender age we need protection and support, freedom and safety in which to become as self-possessed as possible before giving ourselves to anyone else. It is a time to learn what our femininity actually is, so that if we do later choose to share it with a partner or children we will be conscious of what it truly is we are offering. Menarche virginity teaches us to stand alone, to develop a sense of Self as separate, our own possession. It is no small thing to grow into the knowledge that we are *our very own being.* We need this time of virginity to develop our will, to learn to know and trust our own wishes, preferences, decisions and feelings so that we can step into our adult lives with the flame of self-possession already burning brightly inside us. (Sadly, in our virginity-oblivious world too many young women lose their psyche-logical virginity before they ever get to find it – some in covertly patriarchal cultures where they are under huge pressure to project their sexuality in ways they hope will appeal to men

---

27   You can read more about this kind of virginity in *The Moon and the Virgin* by Nor Hall. Published by The Women's Press in London in 1980

and earn them the love they crave, and others in overtly patriarchal ones where women's virginity is considered the possession not of themselves, but of their male family members.)

> In conscious menstruality virginity is lifelong, inalienable, wild and free – ours to possess and renew regardless of whether and how we engage in sexual relationship

If we are willing to own it, virginity is a lifelong, inalienable, wild and free possession, regardless of whether and how we choose to engage in sexual relationships. True virginity can never be 'lost'.[28] Menarche has ushered us into our virginity. Now pre-ovulation will bring us a monthly invitation (or perhaps command) to graduate our virginity into more sophisticated and complex forms. As grown women we are deepening our ability to 'hold our own' not just with ourself, but *within the context of our relationships with others,* including partners and children. We are now asked to be virgin lovers, virgin wives, virgin mothers – learning to live from that self-possessed and self-referenced place within ourselves *at the same time as fulfilling our roles in all our relationships and commitments* – fidelity to self *in balance with* love for others. If this developmental task seems to call for some ingenuity, well and good, for it comes with the cycle phase when our powers of intellect and will are at their sharpest. As with everything in conscious menstruality, there is so much scope for deepening and refining our virginity – and this is why we cycle for many more years than it takes to produce a family. Eventually menopause is going to require an even more advanced form of virginity, so we need many many pre-ovulational opportunities to prepare ourselves to step up for that!

> Pre-ovulational virginity is about learning to live from a self-possessed and self-referenced place **at the same time as fulfilling our roles and commitments in relationships and family life:** fidelity to Self in balance with love for others

---

28 Except when it is taken by sexual abuse or rape, and for girls and women who have been dispossessed in this way support to consciously reclaim their virginity is essential to recovery.

the world within women

Self-sufficiency, a primary quality of virginity, has not been encouraged in women in recent millennia, and consequently is not well understood. It does not mean we are aloof, closed or unloving, but that we do not *need* another to complete our sense of self. Self-sufficient virgins make excellent lovers, partners, spouses and mothers. Their lack of dependence upon another's support for their self-maintenance leaves them free to give and receive abundantly in their relationships out of generosity and gratitude rather than anxiety and need. A true virgin knows she can rely on herself, but that does not mean she will not enjoy the presence and offerings of another.

Many women embark on virgin journeys in their adult lives. Disillusioned with relationships that do not allow them the freedom they desire, do not honour all of whom they are, and do not allow them to grow as they yearn to, they choose to stay on their own for a time. Their quest is to truly discover and claim their virginity, often for the first time if they were not given an awareness of it at menarche. They feel the virginal determination to shape their life according to their own nature, to define their own direction and beliefs, and to act always from that inner source. Only then are they ready to go into their next relationship (including relationship with self) on truly equal terms, bringing their whole, fully-owned potential with them.

a pause to consider…
Honouring my virgin journey

What have been the significant times of aloneness in my life?

What have I received from them? What parts of myself have flourished?

What priority does my virgin journey get in my current life?

What most nourishes and inspires me in my self-development?

Do I get enough of that?

How can I ensure fidelity to my virgin journey now? What does it ask me to do/cherish/prioritise?

Pre–ovulation refreshes us like a frolic in a clear mountain stream. Like morning, like springtime, like waxing moon, it's time to lighten up, open up, receive and expand.

x

At a glance…

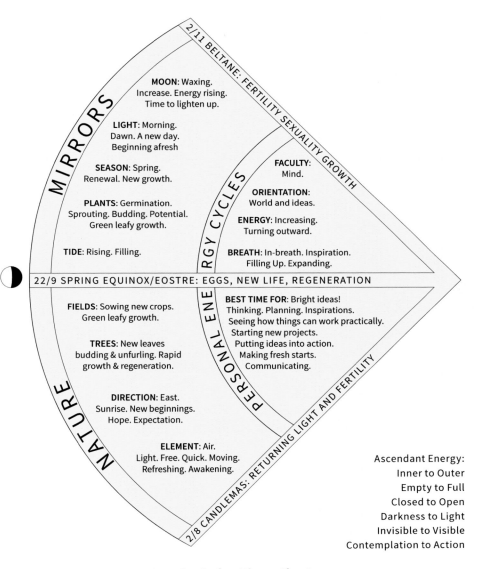

Pre-Ovulation Phase Chart

2/11 BELTANE: FERTILITY SEXUALITY GROWTH

MIRRORS

MOON: Waxing. Increase. Energy rising. Time to lighten up.

LIGHT: Morning. Dawn. A new day. Beginning afresh

SEASON: Spring. Renewal. New growth.

PLANTS: Germination. Sprouting. Budding. Potential. Green leafy growth.

TIDE: Rising. Filling.

ENERGY CYCLES

FACULTY: Mind.

ORIENTATION: World and ideas.

ENERGY: Increasing. Turning outward.

BREATH: In-breath. Inspiration. Filling Up. Expanding.

22/9 SPRING EQUINOX/EOSTRE: EGGS, NEW LIFE, REGENERATION

NATURE

FIELDS: Sowing new crops. Green leafy growth.

TREES: New leaves budding & unfurling. Rapid growth & regeneration.

DIRECTION: East. Sunrise. New beginnings. Hope. Expectation.

ELEMENT: Air. Light. Free. Quick. Moving. Refreshing. Awakening.

PERSONAL ENERGY

BEST TIME FOR: Bright ideas! Thinking. Planning. Inspirations. Seeing how things can work practically. Starting new projects. Putting ideas into action. Making fresh starts. Communicating.

CANDLEMAS: RETURNING LIGHT AND FERTILITY

2/8 CANDLEMAS: RETURNING LIGHT AND FERTILITY

Ascendant Energy:
Inner to Outer
Empty to Full
Closed to Open
Darkness to Light
Invisible to Visible
Contemplation to Action

Energy of expression / action

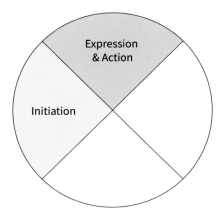

Ovulation, the summer of our menstrual cycle, is a glorious feeling. Energetic, expansive and confident, it is utterly enjoyable, and of course deliciously sexy. In its natural state ovulation is truly a treat to look forward to each month, a time when it is just wonderful to be a woman.

As I write this description I acknowledge with great sadness that it is not the experience of many millions of women in today's world. Ovulational energy has been extinguished for so long, for so many reasons and in so many ways in our world that we no longer realise it is missing, and many of us do not even know what it is. If you are in a situation where the pill or other synthetic hormonal contraception seems the best option for you currently, read these next pages with care and compassion[29]. Take heart, and know that a time is coming when, through knowing our cycle intimately, we will no longer have to resort to ovulation-suppressing, mood-lowering and libido-dulling ways of avoiding pregnancy, and you and millions of other women will once again be free to experience the whole spectrum of your sexual energy. Just imagine what a monthly council of ovulational women could offer in today's world, and the benefits such a liberated feminine energy could bring!

---

29 For those wanting more information about The Pill and other synthetic hormonal contraceptive methods, I strongly recommend Jane Bennett and Alexandra Pope's book *The Pill: Are You Sure it's For You?* Allen & Unwin, Australia, 2008

Ovulation in the holographic femenome

Remembering that the four seasons of our monthly cycle echo the four overall seasons of the femenome, we can see that all the characteristics of ovulation also apply to the whole period of our lives in which we are fertile, even though within those decades we are constantly cycling. So our ovulations are like little summers within the big summer of our life – a delicious double-whammy.

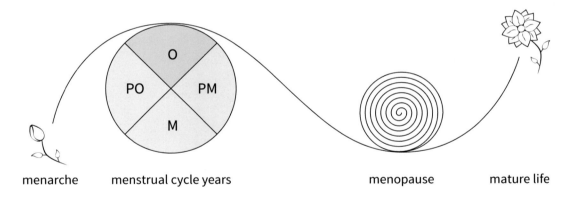

menarche   menstrual cycle years   menopause   mature life

Nature-mirrors at ovulation

Full moon occurs when – and because – the moon is directly opposite the sun (as seen from Earth): the feminine looking the masculine right in the eye, meeting his gaze with her own. She is her most fully realised self – bright and glorious, her whole body illuminated, none of it in shadow. At this time of her month she meets him on symmetrically balanced terms, rising in the east as he sets in the west, setting in the west as he rises in the east, moving in an orbit of perfect complementarity with his.

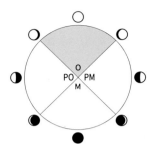

We all know the feeling of full-moon. Everything is heightened, magnified. It's hard to sleep when there's so much light to fire up our energy, awaken us sexually and emotionally, stir us up. Whether our state of mind is joyous or jangling, the full moon will make it more so. With so much big energy around, it's a great time to get things done, day or night.

Full moon is magni-ficent. It magnifies everything!

Maximised light is a recurrent theme at ovulation. The matching part of the dark-light cycle is midday or noon, when the sun is at its zenith and daylight at its peak. It's the busy, active, outward-oriented time of the day, when we like to be fully occupied and achieving our projects. And in the planet's bigger, slower, light-cycle, celebrated by the Celtic seasonal festivals, we are at mid-summer, the fullest extent of daylight, fertility and abundance.

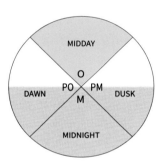

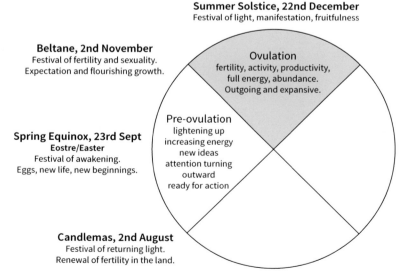

Summer Solstice, 22nd December
Festival of light, manifestation, fruitfulness

Beltane, 2nd November
Festival of fertility and sexuality.
Expectation and flourishing growth.

Ovulation
fertility, activity, productivity,
full energy, abundance.
Outgoing and expansive.

Pre-ovulation
lightening up
increasing energy
new ideas
attention turning
outward
ready for action

Spring Equinox, 23rd Sept
Eostre/Easter
Festival of awakening.
Eggs, new life, new beginnings.

Candlemas, 2nd August
Festival of returning light.
Renewal of fertility in the land.

Seasonal festival Nature mirror for ovulation (southern hemisphere)

the world within women

The light-motif continues with our **directional Nature-mirror** for ovulation, which is **north**,[30] the direction in which Earth's longitudinal lines are expanding, opening up. North is associated for us in the southern hemisphere with the noonday sun, warmth, energy, activity and productivity. And with the ovulational **element, fire,** which is active, powerful, radiant, vital and energetic. Light itself represents the outer, visible world, the rational, physical and practical aspects of life.

All of this light and love has a very potent effect on living things in Nature. Growth, fertility and flowering are all at their peak, energy of all kinds at its most expansive. Even the ocean seems to swell, surging its tides to their highest point along our shores. Fields, gardens and orchards are humming with ripening crops; the weather is warm and generous; everything is lush and abundant…

Personal energy mendala at ovulation

…As are we! It's always helpful for us to know where we are in our cycle, and especially to know exactly when we are ovulating. Although medicine can provide us with technical ways of pin-pointing our ovulation for contraceptive purposes, menstruality itself gives us plenty of natural and easy (and enjoyable) signals that we are fertile through our energy, feelings and sensations. For most women, the ovulational season is about a week long, with gathering intensity over three days, a peak day, and then diminishing intensity over the following three days. Ovulation is a state of sexual arousal. The energies of our body, mind, heart and soul are all primed for touching the divine through connection with the otherness of a beloved. Sexual energy is not something we have been encouraged to explore very deeply, as our cultures strive to emerge from age-old religious and moral fear of it. So it is vitally important that we turn instead to the femenome herself, and the powerful surges of feeling she brings us at ovulation, if we are to get to know who we really are as feminine beings.

---

30 If you live in the northern hemisphere the mendala is flipped so that ovulation aligns with the qualities of south, and menstruation with north.

> The femenome invites us to consciousness through
> energy, feelings and sensations in the body

Ovulation, like female sexuality itself, is a state of complete openness. Desire is at its peak – we yearn to make love – whether we have a partner or not. So, increasingly as our ovulation approaches, and fully as it is occurring, we will have the same secretions of noticeable wetness from our vagina as we do in arousal. We also emanate a particular fragrance from our genital area at ovulation. It is pleasant and worthwhile identifying as a helpful indicator. Some women experience a pain, similar to stitch, or a tenderness in their ovary as the egg is released – this too is very helpful for pinpointing ovulation within the hour of its occurrence.

Other signs we will notice as we attune to our natural ovulational feelings include a delicious expansiveness – of energy, confidence, optimism, enjoyment and self-esteem. Ovulation is like the zoom icon on our computer – it maximises everything. There is often a heightened sense of our own ability, attractiveness and potential. Ovulation does not exaggerate, though – as with each of the cycle's phases, it gives us a particular lens through which to experience aspects of ourselves as we truly are. We are more likely at ovulation than any other part of our month to feel that we are beautiful (as we are) and to wear clothes that enhance our sexuality. Like the midday sun, like full-moon, like the open-hearted flowers of mid-summer, our energy is bright, radiant, full, immense. We can achieve a lot at this time of the month, and it is well worth making the most of this special energy and reaping its rewards.

Because ovulation energy is sexual, it is also strongly connected to our love, sociability and relational capacities. This is the time of our month to remember that the fundamental rhythm of life within us, the most intimate and personal, sacred and essential Nature-mirror of all, is our own heart's beat. Our cycle is an exact replica of our heart's rhythm, but slower, and bigger – one beat per month (so that like slowed-down music, it takes on a deeper tone). The ovulation moment in our cycle resonates with the point where our heart is most open, expanded, receptive of the blood which is our life-source so that it can send this sacred vitality out to every part of our body in an ever-repeating act of love

116   the world within women

and generosity. Not for nothing has humanity always associated love – both the yearning for and the giving of it – with the heart!

Ovulation is mothering energy – ultimately loving, nurturing, giving, generous, other-oriented, supporting the relationship-and-family-raising phase of life that this is for most women. This is the femenome energy we stay in when we pause in our cycle for pregnancy, early motherhood and breast-feeding, with its intense relational and bodily focus, and orientation to another's welfare. Because of its outgoing nature, this energy also provides a wonderful foundation for women actively participating in the world, developing careers and social networks.

Ovulation energy is all about love. It is relational, nurturing, mothering energy

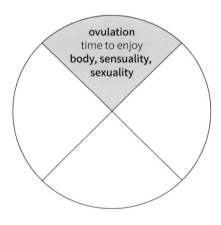

With all this energy, sexuality and activity going on it is easy to recognise that the femenome is shining her spotlight on the **faculty of body** at the ovulational time of the month. So this is a time to revel in our physicality – indulge in sensuality, celebrate our sexuality, exercise with ease, and enjoy the strength and practicality of our body in every possible way. It's a great time to get things done. It is so very important at this time of the month to allow our body to express its love in all the ways it will want to – this may even include making our home clean and shiny, painting the roof, clearing the garden, or inviting guests over for dinner.

Ovulation highlights the faculty of **BODY**

We hear a lot about mindfulness these days, but perhaps not enough about bodyfulness: the art of being fully present in our body. The femenome asks us to **embody** the sacred feminine, to physically **be** that in the world. If we want to get to know what the feminine really is, the reference book to go to is our physical body – the complete and unabridged encyclopaedia of being female.

> Our body is the original, complete and unabridged en-cyclo-paedia of being female (because our cycles reveal everything we need to know about ourselves)

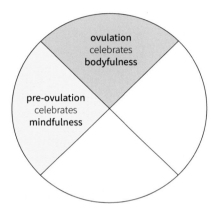

We can really help ourselves to open to the fulsomeness of ovulation's invitations by finding the corresponding place in our breath cycle, and letting it teach us.

a pause to experience...
Breath meditation for ovulation

Find yourself a place that feels big, spacious and free. At this time of the month you might enjoy being on top of hills or mountains, under wide skies, or out in vast expanses. Face north (or south if you are in the northern hemisphere) and feel the huge potential and abundance that radiates from there. As you breathe, let your heart and your whole self open, wide and yet wider, to receive from this generous and boundless source.

the world within women

As you begin to pay attention to your breath notice where your in-breath naturally stops and turns to begin the out-breath. Just pay attention to that rhythm for a few breaths. Now, on your next in-breath, notice again this natural turning point, but this time go past it a little, allowing your in-breath to continue into an even fuller expansion of your rib-cage. Make this your new turning point, so that each breath is longer, deeper, more filling. Feel your capacity to receive more than you normally do.

Now, with ease and gentleness, begin to create just the slightest of pauses at the top of each in-breath. Let this continue for a few breaths until your body is fully relaxed into this permission.

Begin paying closer attention to the sensation of fullness as you pause. Let those pauses lengthen a little, so you can really start to experience just what it is that a full breath does inside you. Can you feel the subtle tingle of oxygen stimulating your cells, energising them? Breathe and pause… breathe and pause… let your long, slow in-breaths push against the inside of your skin, stretching you…

When you really let yourself feel it, how big is the expanse inside you? Your love? Your potential? Your desires? How big are you? Don't be modest – believe what you feel!

This is your ovulational energy, all you and all yours. Breathe. Believe. Enjoy. Savour this energy, get to know it. Drink deep, and let it fill you. Consciously spend time in its company at least once in every cycle. Let it inspire you, fill you with hope and confidence in your potential. And, when you finish your meditation, take its expansiveness with you into your life.

The quintessential Nature-mirror teacher for ovulation

As we have already seen, it is the flowering phase in the life cycle of plants that matches ovulation on our mendala.

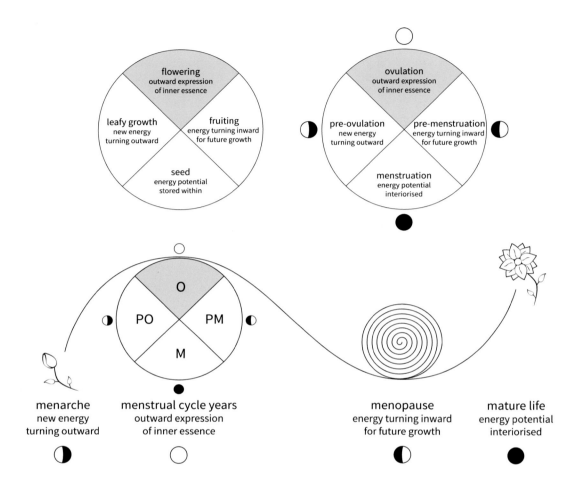

flowering outward expression of inner essence		**ovulation** outward expression of inner essence
leafy growth new energy turning outward	**fruiting** energy turning inward for future growth	**pre-ovulation** new energy turning outward
	seed energy potential stored within	

menarche
new energy
turning outward

menstrual cycle years
outward expression
of inner essence

menopause
energy turning inward
for future growth

mature life
energy potential
interiorised

I want to introduce you now to the teacher who has opened my eyes more than any other to the ovulational aspect of our nature. Consider a green bush growing in your garden. It has roots in the earth, green or brown stems rising up from them, and glossy green leaves arrayed upon those. A beautiful being. And then one day something absolutely extraordinary happens…

Imagine for a moment that you had never before seen a pink flower emerging from a green bush – that you had never learned to take such a miracle for granted. What would you make of it? What is a bush actually *doing* when it produces a flower? And what *is* a flower? What exactly *is* the impulse that causes this exquisite form, quite different in appearance from the rest of the bush, to arise from inside it? What causes a bird to burst into song? A glow-worm to glow? A rose to exude fragrance? And speaking of fragrance – what unspeakable soul language is *that*?

All of these marvels of Nature have the same energetic form. They are emanations, revelations, manifestations of something ineffable, some divine essence or soul, from inside living beings. They are irrepressible ex-pressions (pressing outward) of what is carried within. We *know* this feeling, this moment, this outburst of what is most essential, refined and holy from the secret/sacred source at our centre. The form of a flower, the gesture of its opening, its procreative role all tell us – the flower is the orgasm, the ecstasy, the love-rapture of the plant, responding to the kiss of light. It is the fertility of the plant, the impulse that is too exuberant to contain, so that some spills over to make new life possible.

Now while we are talking about fertility, it is most important to recall that while the femenome does include the marvellous fertility that makes babies, that is not its only fertility. We have far more ovulations (perhaps up to 500) than we would ever want children! So we need to ask, *what else* is our fertility for? What about those of us who are not in sexual relationships, or do not want babies, but still go through this wildly sexual time of arousal every month? Sometimes it's hard to know what to do with so much energy, and how to let it flow rather than getting trapped in frustration. These are important questions. Learning to own, enjoy and express our sexuality *just for ourselves* can feel like uncharted territory – and indeed it has been forbidden territory for thousands of years – but what might happen if we try tapping in to it? If we get to know all of what it is, and what it is for, beyond what we know already? What else might happen if we open to it as a collective energy? We need to see our glory mirrored in other women, and share wild, exuberant ovulation celebrations if we are to let this energy out, ride the tiger, know what it is that is coursing through us.

> Ovulation is our flowering time of the month

We flower at ovulation. That glorious sense of expansiveness that fills us so full it presses against the inside of our skin is, quite literally, the energy of ex-pression: the natural emanation of our inner essence wanting to manifest itself into the world, in beauty, in love, and in action. Flowers can teach us a lot about how to carry our feminine grace 'out loud' in the world. Flowers never worry about whether they will be too yellow or the wrong red. They just open up and show their beauty. This can be hard for us to do, because we have been taught by aeons of religious and misguided morality that feminine beauty and sexuality are not to be trusted, and certainly not to be flaunted. Flowers flaunt, because they fully own their beauty. They don't compare, or worry, or try to conform. They are free to be themselves, and therefore effortlessly beautiful, an infinitely valuable gift to the world. When we women can relax into our ovulational confidence we remember that real beauty is not to be gained by product or regime, but by letting the femininity that is inside us shine out. The secrets to this are very simple, but that doesn't mean they are easy to learn. We have a lot of conditioning to get past, and, as always, the femenome will ask us to go beyond the usual limits of our cultural approval.

a pause to reflect...
What is the purpose of our beauty?

To know the purpose of our beauty we can learn from every other beauty in the world – flowers, birdsong, Nature, music, colour, poetry, and everything else in this boundless catalogue. Beauty uplifts us, quite literally, creating an altered state of consciousness, an opened heart energy, an awakened and heightened spiritual awareness and response from the expansion of the sharply indrawn breath (gasp) that comes involuntarily when we encounter something beautiful or inspiring.

What beauties am I aware of and willing to name, claim and fully own in myself, without hiding or avoidance?

How might I consciously express these from now on in my daily life?

When / where / how might it be difficult for me to stay connected to my beauty?

How can I increase my confidence and trust in the beautiful aspects of myself?

What can I offer others and the world by being willing to be beautiful?

How might I carry my beauty with ease and enjoyment in the world, as flowers do?

Special features of the ovulation phase

Embodiment

Let's remember again that the femenome, our own innate femininity, is actually a mystical path. But here is the magic: like all true mystical paths, it asks us not to *transcend* our body, but to *fully inhabit it*. In the sacred school of the femenome we learn through *experiences* that are ordinary, simple, immediate and taught via energy, sensation and feelings in our human female body. Really, this is the most wonderful, exciting and liberating secret to awaken to – the sublimely divine and utterly ordinary art of *just being ourselves*. Our body is the vehicle through which we *express* our love, our intention, our natural wish to manifest our desires in *action* as physical beings in a physical world. What we *do* is who we *are* made manifest.

> The femenome is a mystical path asking us not to transcend our body **but to fully inhabit it**

Enjoying Ourselves

How often do you really, fully, just enjoy being yourself? Ovulation is the time of the month when we are most likely to be able to suspend our inner critic, stop worrying about everything we think is not perfect about us, and feel good about ourselves. This feeling, all by itself, is the best medicine ever, bringing huge physiological and psyche-logical benefits to us and everyone around us. Yet it can be strangely unfamiliar to us, and we may find we need to actually study this art and practice it with a delicious diligence every month until we are completely addicted.

An ovulational invitation

Over the next few months, be very open to ways of enjoying **yourself:** who you are, what you love, how you feel, what you do. Make sure you set aside enjoying-time each day of your ovulation phases. You may need to jot down some reminders in your journal or on your mendala.

How can you factor in bliss, sensuality and deliciousness? Simply sitting for five minutes in your own good company, fully feeling the sensations of ovulational optimism may be a good start.

Or you might play around with doing things in a deliberately ovulational way

Ask the question, 'who am I?' and let your O energy answer it – in colour, words, dance, sound, movement

Open your heart to the O-vibe and bring it with you into everything you do over those few days

Walk womanly

Be your fullest self in your connections with others

Laugh and play

Wear your most ovulational outfits

Feel gorgeous

Dare to take your sexiness everywhere, just so you can delight in it

Be sure you don't let busyness or responsibility distract you from the delicious sensations in your body – indulge in them

Dance with life

Hum and sing your way through chores

Love your body's strength and accomplishments

Be daring

Let your O-energy organise your life while it's around

Love who you are – get to know her better

Grow a bigger and bigger repertoire of ways to enjoy being you

What if we could be as dedicated, as committed and diligent in enjoying ourselves as we are toward other tasks in our lives?

I am just adding one note here, not so much of *caution* as of *awareness*. It is important to *engage with* our ovulation energy, not to abandon ourselves to it. Especially sexually. I remember so vividly occasions when my wild ovulational optimism assured me that making love would be so wonderful and beautiful and everything would be okay – only to be aghast the very next week as my pre-menstrual anxiety fixated on the risk of an unplanned pregnancy. So, in your bold and uninhibited ovulational adventures, make sure some part of you is taking care of the delicate line between freedom and riskiness. Maybe your sensible pre-ovulation self can come up with a plan for you. (My solution was to make sure my lovers were aware of my ovulational tendency to throw caution to the wind, and willing to take extra care at this time. They did, bless their hearts, and all was well.)

Being full of ourselves

Were you ever told in childhood (or even later) not to be too 'full of yourself'? It is such a pity we all get that message – what better thing could there possibly be to be full of than our own Self? The whole purpose of the femenome over our lifetime is to make us quite literally full of conscious, connected Self, and ovulation with its natural expansiveness and confidence is the prime time to develop this virtue!

a pause to reflect ...
Embodying the universal feminine

What would it feel like to wake up again to our right and responsibility as women to embody nothing less than the divine feminine in the world? What would that ask of us?

What is my sexuality, and what is it for?

How do I express this into the world through my physical form?

What is in me that wants to flower in this way?

How well do I take care of the feminine within me?

What would I like to do more to allow, express, honour and enjoy my femininity in my daily life, and especially at my ovulation times?

Take your time to be detailed in your answers to these questions. And keep returning to them as you learn and develop more and more fully into your deep feminine Self. The world needs **us** to bring much more feminine energy into influence for the sake of its future.

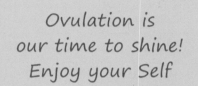

Ovulation is
our time to shine!
Enjoy your Self

x

At a glance…

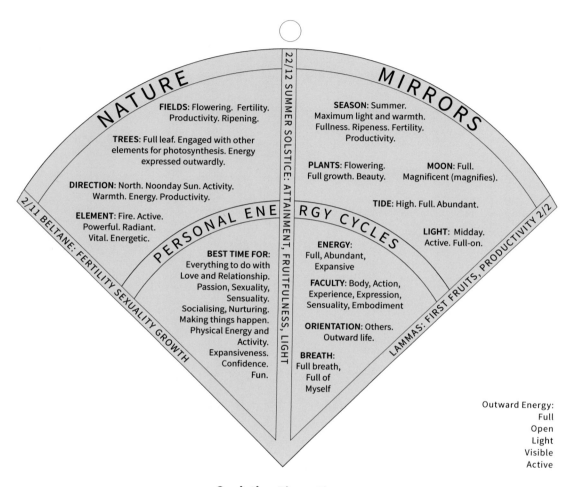

NATURE

FIELDS: Flowering. Fertility. Productivity. Ripening.

TREES: Full leaf. Engaged with other elements for photosynthesis. Energy expressed outwardly.

DIRECTION: North. Noonday Sun. Activity. Warmth. Energy. Productivity.

ELEMENT: Fire. Active. Powerful. Radiant. Vital. Energetic.

MIRRORS

SEASON: Summer. Maximum light and warmth. Fullness. Ripeness. Fertility. Productivity.

PLANTS: Flowering. Full growth. Beauty.

MOON: Full. Magnificent (magnifies).

TIDE: High. Full. Abundant.

LIGHT: Midday. Active. Full-on.

PERSONAL ENERGY CYCLES

BEST TIME FOR: Everything to do with Love and Relationship. Passion, Sexuality, Sensuality. Socialising, Nurturing. Making things happen. Physical Energy and Activity. Expansiveness. Confidence. Fun.

ENERGY: Full, Abundant, Expansive

FACULTY: Body, Action, Experience, Expression, Sensuality, Embodiment

ORIENTATION: Others. Outward life.

BREATH: Full breath, Full of Myself

22/12 SUMMER SOLSTICE: ATTAINMENT, FRUITFULNESS, LIGHT

2/11 BELTANE: FERTILITY SEXUALITY GROWTH

LAMMAS: FIRST FRUITS, PRODUCTIVITY 2/2

Outward Energy:
Full
Open
Light
Visible
Active

Ovulation Phase Chart

CHAPTER SEVEN

Dark side of the moon: bringing consciousness to our inner life

What does the phrase 'dark side of the moon' mean to you? It is a most fascinating thing that the moon, our faithful mirror of the feminine, is actually as much a presence of darkness as of light. In the monthly dance of her waxing and waning, her unlit, invisible faces are there in our sky in exactly equal though ever-changing measure with the familiar yet also ever-changing shapes of her light aspects. And so it is with us. The time it takes for the complete balance and interplay of light and dark, visible and invisible, outer and inner elements of our nature to be experienced is, just like the moon's, one menstrual cycle.

It is important not to be afraid of the dark side of our moon, and wise to check whether we are carrying any negative connotations we may have absorbed, perhaps unconsciously, around these words. It is true that the design of the femenome will purposely turn us toward our shadow side for the third and fourth phases of our cycle each month. Unfortunately the term 'shadow' has also gathered some negative interpretations over the years. But our shadow side is not our 'bad' side. It is simply the parts of us that are, to varying degrees, unknown – out of our awareness, not yet developed, not owned, integrated or fully conscious within us. Because these aspects have not been allowed to be part of our life – have not received the love, understanding, attention, acceptance and support they deserve – like any rejected child they will throw temper tantrums or whatever it takes to **make** us feel their presence and need. This does **not** mean we are bad, mad, wrong or sick. It means that important parts of our self are knocking at the door of our awareness. They may have been distorted or put under unbearable pressure by being held out of awareness – which is why some of the feelings arising in us at our pre-menstrual time can feel volcanic!

There are two transitions in the femenome that are often experienced as problematic for women – the shift from ovulation to pre-menstruation in our cycle, and the great change from our cycle years into menopause. When we look at these in the map of the whole femenome, we can immediately see that they occur in both the monthly cycle and the metacycle on the cusp between the light side and the dark side of the moon. Big energy exists on these cusp lines, because they are a threshold between one kind of consciousness and another.

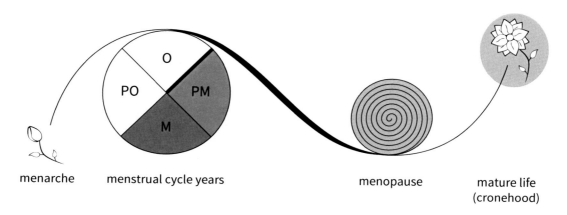

menarche   menstrual cycle years   menopause   mature life
                                                                              (cronehood)

Big energy needs to be met by equally big awareness if it is not to get us into trouble. So it is vital that we remember to bring our conscious menstruality tools and a real spirit of curious enquiry into these mysteries:

?

Why are these particular transitions so commonly difficult for us? *What is really trying to happen* at these times? The answers are complex, beautiful and profound (and we will learn much more about them in the next books, on menopause and the overall femenome). For now, to keep things simple in this small handbook, let's just say that these two transitions are problematic **because they are pushing us up against the limits of what our cultures currently understand and can deal with.** We are unsupported at these times, because most of us have grown up in societies that have developed along purely masculine lines, where the rational and practical qualities of mind and body have been valued above the ir-rational and more feminine ones of feeling, intuition and spirituality. But if we can find the fenomenal courage to take the ride, we will discover that there *is* a steady hand at the helm; that we *are* on course for an intended destination, despite the swirls and eddies of these big currents.

> Pre-menstruation and menopause are crossings into the ir-rational (beyond-rational) realms of life

At these times the femenome is taking us beyond the reach of mind, the faculty we have been taught to value and trust above all others, into lesser-known territory where we are not (yet) so comfortable or at ease. The dark side of the moon is our inner life, and the femenome, being the guardian of our wholeness, completion and balance, is ensuring that we engage with the inward, soulful aspects of our development as much as with the outward energies that fit more easily into our world as it is.

> The femenome is the missing piece that can take us beyond the psycho-logical and into the psyche-logical. Psyche-logic brings soul dimensions into ordinary, everyday life

To understand what doesn't make sense to logic, we have to look *further* than logic can see (and this is where science-based medicine has totally failed women). To help us accomplish this, the femenome very cleverly insists that we go into the dark each month, and in a major way at midlife, *so that we cannot avoid learning to navigate by the inner faculties that would otherwise remain undeveloped inside us.* Women have a natural access (even if we don't always like it) to the vital interior faculties that the world is short of, through the doorways opened in us every month by our hormones. It is this that makes us the muse we are to men (see p 103).

So what *is* darkness? It is all too easy to define it as the *absence* of light – as what it is not. But what would a moonflower say the darkness *is*? *What is it in the darkness* that calls her out of her tightly furled bud? And *what is it in her own nature* that answers with such exuberance? Moonflowers open with an astounding speed and vigour once night comes (if you have not seen them flinging their petals wide in their uniquely ecstatic way, do watch this stunning spectacle on the internet) that must surely qualify them to be the quintessential teachers of the mysterious potency of darkness.

In the deep wisdom of many cosmologies across the world, everything begins in a great void, in darkness: the cosmic pregnancy; the beginning before the beginning. As a keen mountaineer in my younger years I spent many a wide-awake night in a tiny tent perched in high and remote mountain places, listening to a mysterious and utterly captivating phenomenon. Even out there, far beyond the noise of any human contrivance, higher than any water could flow, and long after the day's wind had calmed to utter stillness – at the heart of the greatest silence to be found on earth, still there was sound. What *was* that unexplained hum, that timeless vibration deep below the threshold of ordinary hearing, and only perceptible when everything else had ceased? We could never hear it by day, no matter how we listened for it. But as each night's darkness magnified nothingness, there it would be again. The sound of the planet turning in space? The original tone of Life Itself, keeping all things in motion? The reverberation of eternity pulsing within time?

We too have this frequency humming within us, our own soul's potency, visible only in darkness, audible only in silence, discernible only in emptiness. This is quite literally the vibration of our life's *potential* – everything held available for when we have the consciousness to use it. Every woman knows that life begins on the inside long before it is visible on the outside. Because it compels us to live half of our lives on the dark side of the moon, the femenome holds the potential, as we noted above, for us to advance our consciousness beyond the limits our culture has currently reached. What we are doing when we practise conscious menstruality is bringing back into the world the essential feminine element that has been missing for too long – the dimension of **interiority** and access to the much bigger consciousness we embody when we include *all* of our Self. In this way, through initiating women into personal maturation and consciousness, the femenome is also working for all humanity.

> The femenome holds in its design the potential to advance our consciousness beyond the limits of current cultural development – not just for each woman personally but, through the initiation of women, for all humanity

Going beyond the known is no easy task, as any intrepid explorer knows. Pioneering is never comfortable, and often lonely. It will not feel normal. On the dark side of the moon the femenome initiates us by hormonal prompts that push us, mentally, physically, emotionally and spiritually, right up against the edges of our 'normal' world – because it is only on those borders that we will find the doorways we need to take us further than we've been before. The rest of this chapter will begin our quest to understand the mysterious navigational aids the femenome presents us with on the dark side of the moon, so that we get to travel freely and confidently through the whole spectrum of our feminine potential.

A pause to contemplate …
Moonflower meditation for the dark side of the moon

Make yourself a very comfortable resting or reclining place in preparation for your next crossing into the dark side of your cycle. As far as is possible, arrange for this to be a place where you can be in darkness, and in silence. And do ensure that you are familiar with the miraculous ways of moonflowers blossoming in the dark (either from watching the process in the real or on the internet).

When your cycle's dark side of the moon arrives (two or three nights into your pre-menstrual phase would be perfect, or if you do not have a visible cycle, at the time when the moon has waned down to half) go to your prepared place. Extinguish any light that you may have brought in with you, and simply sit or lie there. Breathe softly in a way that gradually attunes you to darkness as a presence, not an absence. What is it like for you to be surrounded by this profound and attentive presence? Can you quieten a little more, allowing a stillness to settle inside you, so you can pay total attention to the presence of darkness? What does it show you, tell you, offer you as it folds itself around you? As you breathe breaths of its essence into yourself? Allow plenty of time for just getting acquainted with darkness, as intimately and trustfully as you can.
And now, as your daylight busyness and preoccupations fall away, and you become

fully present to the dark, give yourself over into the tutelage of your moonflower Nature mirror. Now that you are quiet enough to hear answers that would be inaudible in the clamour of daylight life, breathe your way into her world. What is that extra-ordinary thing that happens for her, and in her, only in darkness? Let yourself enquire of her, what is it inside her stems, her petals, her soul, that awakens, stirs, opens and blossoms only at the touch of darkness? That responds so ardently under its influence? And what is that same thing in us, lying in wait to become beautiful, luminous, fragrant and open, that only the darkness can trigger? What wants to surprise us by flowering differently here, in the place where we are not expecting blossoms? What other-worldly fragrance lies in potential here, even just for our own soul to inhale?

Lie back in the quiet, with your face turned to the potent darkness, and allow the secret and mystical blossoming of the moonflower you are at this time of your month.

Fenomenology 203: Pre-menstruation

Energy of reflection and discernment

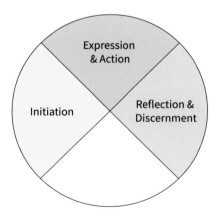

So now, as the pages of this book turn just like the days of our month, we find ourselves at a time of particular mystery and sensitivity in the workings of the femenome. As we have seen, crossing the cusp in our cycle between ovulation and pre-menstruation is a delicate business. It is the time of the month when we are most in need of care and consciousness as we step into parts of our feminine nature, and indeed the Laws of Nature, that are least understood and accepted, and therefore especially unsupported by the cultures in which we live.

In my courses and workshops at Luna House, I have felt my heart ache as I observe time and time again that when the moment comes for women to describe their pre-menstrual selves, everything changes in the room. Without exception there is a darkening, a hardening, a change in voice tone, a sense that women have moved away from tender connection with their experience into a rather condemning and disliking stance. The descriptions are unremittingly negative: at best, a harsh kind of humour, and at worst a secret, painful distress and self-blame.

Women often feel they are *not themselves* in their pre-menstrual (and menopausal) times. But we can't be not-ourselves. We can only be not what we *thought* or *hoped* ourselves to be. The shadow voices we might encounter at these sensitive menstruality moments are the *unpermitted* parts of ourselves emerging, as our hormones thin our defences and our tolerance of what is not ok for us. Sometimes we do not like the parts of ourselves that erupt in these hormone-provoked revelations. Usually others do not like them either, and may criticise, ridicule or reject them. Often, indeed, they are parts of us that have suffered grievously and genuinely, but have never been given the attention they deserve because they have been judged over-the-top, irrational, scary or unfeminine. Anger, hurt, irritation, truth-telling, self-prioritising and sadness often fall into this category, and become deeply buried under layers of shame and disowning. But the more we are aware of and willing to engage with these truthful feelings, the less our hormones will need to create storms of protest to get our attention, because we will respond quickly and clearly to their first murmurs. We will believe their prompts enough to want to seek the *causes* of our premenstrual irritability and attend to them before they turn into rage or despair. We will trust the femenome enough to want to co-operate with its mission of making us whole, real and honest in our emotional lives.

We know from our studies earlier in this book that the virtually universal suffering of women in the pre-menstrual phase is not our fault. That it occurs because we genuinely do not know how to meet the invitations (or perhaps they feel more like commands) that the femenome issues to us as we traverse the shift in our cycle from ovulation into a very different purpose. It is as if we are being sent down a dark stairway without a light to guide our steps – well of course we are going to find that difficult!

a pause to consider ...

Before reading any further (and making sure you have your menstruality journal or a mendala with you) settle into a comfortable position with this page open on your lap. You might like to let your hands rest on the book to give you a way of staying connected with your intention. Let your breath soften into an absolute permission to feel what you feel. Allow a few moments, dropping further and further in to that permission, so that it spreads with ease to every part of your body.

Now, with your attention and receptivity fine-tuned to accept whatever feelings might be present – no matter how secret or subtle – begin to acknowledge as truthfully as you can how it is for you to come to this chapter, and how much this reflects your feelings each month as you come to the pre-menstruation phase of your cycle. Be very allowing of any sensations you may experience, such as sinking, withdrawal, darkening or contracting, or even sadness. See if you can let go of any negative interpretations you may be tempted to make of such feelings. They are perfectly natural – indeed they are in accordance with the Laws of Nature at this time of the life cycle we mirror in our months.

Remember, because of the long history of cultural misunderstandings of our cycle, we have been left with no guidelines or signposts to help us navigate this crossing. We haven't even had our own company on the way as we have struggled to do our best with it. So bring yourself that company now. Breathe yourself some care and curiosity to make sure no judgement or criticism can creep in. Let your in-breaths enquire, and your out-breaths bring the answers from within you – what do you experience at this time of your month? What questions do you have? What do you hope to find in the next few pages? If you were about to walk down a dark stairway, or explore an unknown passage, what exactly would you like to take with you to help you know where you are and see your way? From yourself? From around you? What would support you the most?

Write all the feelings, needs and hopes down. Let them matter, because they do. Keep them in your journal or mendala. They will become your guides. Take some time to describe, draw and get acquainted with the things you have chosen to take with you. Trust your choices, even if you don't quite know yet how to use them.

Because of the unspoken rules of society that we live and behave *at all times as if we were in our ovulation mode,* pre-menstruation and menstruation are inevitably the most stressed and distressed parts of our cycle, the times where we are most compelled to go against our energetic flow. The inward pull of the femenome, as we move on from the summery feelings of ovulation and into the more sensitive and inner-attuned phase of pre-menstruation, goes against the cultural grain. We have been so deeply conditioned to try to be consistent, to trust our heads more than our hearts, to put others' needs ahead of our own, to believe that 'the real world' is the one around us rather than the one inside us. So at the point when our menstruality makes it well-nigh impossible to do any of those things any more, we are highly vulnerable to feeling bad about ourselves and unconsciously falling into internalised resistance to the change that is trying to happen inside us.

Not at all surprisingly, this collision of forces, the argument between our natural inclination to go inward and slowly, and 'normality's' pressure to stay outward and busy, tends to manifest for many of us as irritability, anger, depression, heightened or pent-up emotions and all manner of not-good-enough feelings about our performance. Our moods change because our energy changes, *but our lifestyles do not allow that, and demand we stay the same.* We are therefore set at odds with ourselves energetically. How could we not become irritated, easily upset, tired?

> Our moods change because our energy changes but our lifestyles do not allow that and demand we stay the same

The line that we cross at this time of the month is a most important and purposeful one in the overall femenome design. It can feel as if we step through a door, and into another world – and in many ways that is exactly what does happen. For it is at this point that the femenome, the potter at the wheel of our making, turns her attention to our *inner* shaping. In the perfect plan of our Self-perfecting cycle pre-menstruation and menstruation have the opposite gravitational pull to that of pre-ovulation and ovulation. Now we are asked to bring all our energy *inward* to balance the learning and experiencing we have been enjoying in our *outward-attuned* cycle phases. Every Nature-mirror reassures us that true growth and progression will always require an inward or withdrawing phase to match its outward thrusts. Even so, it is hard for us to actually allow this particular change to happen. Our energy will feel less, because we are accustomed to measuring it on outward productivity rather than recognising its inner dimensions. And because that energy has gone inside us to connect with our inner lives, we are more likely to feel the challenge of our own needs vying for attention in amongst our habitual focus on everyone else's.

Pre-menstruation in the holographic femenome

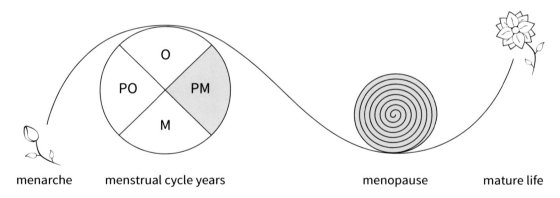

menarche   menstrual cycle years   menopause   mature life

The metacycle phase corresponding to pre-menstruation is menopause. Both are times of ir-rationality: inward-turning focus, heightened feeling, deepening connection with self, and the challenges of contracting energy. I have often heard menopausal women lament that they feel pre-menstrual all the time! The art of conscious menstruality invites us to become adept at our pre-menstrual lessons, so that we are well prepared to graduate into

the world within women

menopause, when that time comes, with ease and assurance. The femenome's actions within us at these times are alchemic in nature – intense, transformational, and deeply rewarding.

Nature-mirrors at pre-menstruation

What can we learn from our Nature-mirrors at pre-menstruation? There is always a poignancy as we feel the first intimations of autumn, and wish we could keep the pleasures of summer going for longer. Certain truths have to be faced – our days are going to shorten and cool. The lush green growth and flowery beauty we have been enjoying is ending. Leaves, no longer required for drawing light into their trees, change in colour and begin to fall from their branches, revealing the 'bare bones' underneath. The ebbing tide too will uncover things that can surprise us. Some of them may be sharp or have a pungent smell, like the feelings we can have in our pre-menstrual time; strange rocks and plants now shown to us so we can learn about them before they are once again covered by the flood-tide of our next ovulation. Flowers have completed their summer task of attracting bees, and are now transforming themselves into a further purpose: becoming fruit. People and animals turn to tasks of harvesting, gathering and storing what has been produced during Nature's time of ex-pression – now it is the season of im-pression, the inward processing of what has been experienced.

Darkness is on the increase, as the days shorten and nights lengthen, or in the lunar cycle, as the moon wanes down a little more each night. Darkness brings a more contemplative feel to life – there is less time for activity, and we are more inside our houses, as if symbolic of our need to also be more oriented within ourselves.

There is an inescapable feeling on this side of all the Nature-mirrors, of going in and going down. It takes care and consciousness not to react to this sensation in an intolerant way, as there is a strong inclination in our cultures to interpret up as good, and down as bad – look no further than your own thumb to see how automatic and unquestioned this has become for us (thumbs-up means favourable, thumbs-down not so). The femenome is in itself a magnificent Law of Nature, and in Nature there are not 'better' and 'worse' parts of the whole – each is essential, and uniquely purposeful. It is true, however, that pre-menstruation and menstruation form the *negative* polarity of our cycle – and indeed that the feminine is the *negative* energetic polarity of humanity. So our quest for conscious menstruality asks us to understand 'the negative' on its own terms, which are the same as those of Nature. Quite simply, as electricity shows us, the negative is the interiorising pole, the receptive principle, the one that draws energy into itself, embracing, containing and transforming it.

We are therefore in our natural energetic element when we go into our pre-menstrual phase. This may come as a surprise to us, as so often, sadly, we feel anything but at home there. It is only because we have been covertly taught to despise and distrust the feminine qualities of sensitivity, inwardness, ir-rationality, quietness, darkness, mystery, softness and slowness that we unconsciously fight them when our cycle draws us into their mysterious realm at pre-menstruation.

It is hard, in our busy lives, to allow the slowing of pace that the femenome requires of us at this time. We really do need the constant presence, teaching and encouragement of our Nature-mirrors to remind us that slowing-down, letting-go, descending, are just as productive and essential to life as activity. Perhaps the Celtic lore of seasonal festivals that matches our month so beautifully would suggest that the fruits of our labours are now ripe for the picking… however, if we don't take the time to harvest them, they will fall and rot and go to waste.

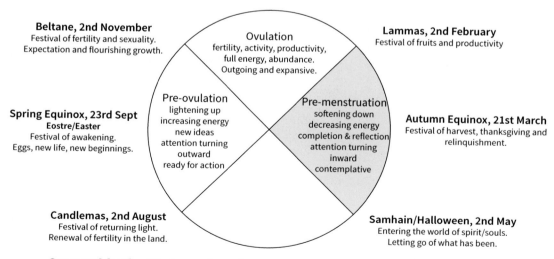

Seasonal festival Nature mirror for pre-menstruation (southern hemisphere)

the world within women

Evening may be the best time for our daily meditation, contemplation, yoga/tai chi/ qui gong, or recreation at this time of the month, being perfectly energetically matched to our pre-menstrual state – a most kindly and beneficent teacher. Feel the name, even-ing. What is Nature doing? She is *evening out* daylight and darkness, bringing them into perfect balance. And evening naturally turns our gaze and our attention to the **west**, the **direction** of sunset: relinquishment, maturity, review, moving toward completion, ending, letting go…

a pause to reflect…

Get ready for your next pre-menstrual time by choosing a place where you can be comfortable and well supported for an evening reverie. Let it be west-facing, with a view of where the sun sets in your part of the world…

What is it like for you to feel a day ending? Often we are so pressured and pre-occupied with too many things to do that we don't really get to experience the natural slowdown that Nature invites as the light fades. What if we could allow ourselves the delicious feeling of putting it all down at the end of a day? Imagine what it might be like to make this a commitment, a special treat for you to prioritise during your pre-menstrual week ~ a conscious attunement ~ an antidote to the stress wind-up that can so easily take us over at this delicate time of the month.

Let yourself simply sit in your special pre-menstrual place, wherever you have chosen it to be, and feel the even-ing of light and darkness, the sweet and calming blend that we call twi-light – be**twi**xt or between-light. Feel the fulcrum, the balance-point, where both these graces are present at the same time.

What would you like to bring with you from your day into the coming night? And then, what would you like to breathe away, acknowledge, learn from and release, so it will not burden your morning? What is there to be thankful for in the day now passing? And what would you like to request of the night, the darkness that is so gently gathering around you moment by moment?

This is the time to allow yourself the benefit of going into your night open and conscious, respect-full and request-full – not overwhelmed by or holding on to the preoccupations of your day. How often do you pause and ask for what you would like to receive from a night? Have you let yourself be aware of the darkness as having something particular and enhancing to offer you? Let yourself see your night-consciousness standing out there on that western horizon with her arms open to all that has occurred in your day. Feel her willingness to hold those things gently. Let all effort fade away softly with the departing light. Rest and breathe.

Water is our Nature-mirror **element** for pre-menstruation. Deep and cool, cleansing and soothing, powerful and penetrating, water embodies reflections, so that we can see things from the opposite direction to our accustomed one. As we know, there is nothing like pre-menstrual energy to turn things upside down! Water loves flow and movement. It is transformational by nature, often being the alchemical element that brings about profound change or completion of a process ('just add water'!). Water can soften what has hardened, refresh what is wilting. Its life-giving presence can penetrate right into the core of things, 'the heart of the matter'. Water carries away what is spent, cleans the slate.

And water is a teacher for us in another way as well. As its rate of flow slows down, water begins to feel the weight of its sediment – anything it is carrying that burdens, irritates or discolours it. The very act of slowing down, as if enabling the water to recognise what is not really part of itself, allows all that is extraneous to drift to the bottom, leaving the water itself clean, clear and pure, true to its original nature. It is for this reason that we need to be very accepting of ourselves when we know we are resisting – not just resigning ourselves to being resistant, but *accepting of ourselves* in the resistant place! Resistance, like depression (which is a particular form of resistance) means that something is not yet understood enough, or supported enough, for us to be able to move on. It slows us down until there *is* enough understanding and support for the weighty particles to be recognised and dissolved or resolved, so the flow of our energy can move on again. If we are willing to stay awake and engaged in it rather than giving up and letting it take charge, the slowness of resistance or depression can help to ensure we don't miss anything out, or leave anything behind, so that our healing is thorough and genuine every step of the way.

Like pre-ovulation, pre-menstruation is a dynamic, transitional phase – a time of rapid change inside us, which of course can feel unsettling. And because its energy movement goes quite strongly downward – the direction that is less popular, less understood, less welcome in our cultural background – we do tend to be alarmed by, or at least wary of, its surges.

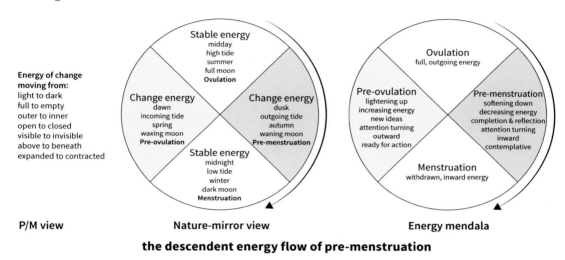

the descendent energy flow of pre-menstruation

This really can be a tricky thing to manage, as the demands of our lives do not quieten or slow down, no matter how much our own energy does. The crucially important thing is to be gently alert to any resistance we might accidentally put up in our efforts to cope with what still has to be done. It is so, so tempting in the face of those demands, to harden up, get a grip, grit our teeth and brace our whole body in the alarm of feeling our natural energy slipping away from us. If we are not very care-full we will automatically reach for the adrenalised energy of sheer determination, or even, just possibly, of angry reactivity at how unfair it all feels. (And yes, it *is* unfair that our natural need to slow down is utterly and completely ignored in the lives we are asked to lead - acknowledging this for ourselves can be surprisingly helpful in keeping us out of the clench of reactive resistance).

As with everything in our practise of conscious menstruality, our breath is an ever-present guide and source of support to us in the simplest and most effective ways. This is especially important when we are up against the inevitable clashes of our cycle-needs with the demands of our everyday lives. At pre-menstruation the out-breath is our energetic match, and can serve us well as an instant first-aid measure in moments of pressure or stress. It is also deliciously therapeutic as the subject of a longer and more luxurious meditation – ideally at evening, but any time is good. I do very strongly recommend you build a regular out-breath practise of some kind into your pre-menstrual week. Most, if not all pre-menstrual distresses, be they physical, mental, emotional or spiritual, are caused, or at least exacerbated, by holding: holding of breath, holding of tension, holding against feelings, holding against awareness. Our out-breath, if done with consciousness and care, is the supreme antidote to this, and can bring immediate and immense relief. So simple, inexpensive and readily available!

It may be hard to believe and trust that such a small thing could make any worthwhile difference to life. It is incredibly easy to under-estimate and under-utilise breath, and the whole way our western culture is driven to do and to get more, more, more, has almost banished the out-breath side of our natural balance from our daily experience. To get the feeling of how much this doesn't work, try taking a good deep in-breath, and then, without breathing out, another. Then, still without breathing out, breathe in yet again – how are you doing so far? I am sure you will find the results speak for themselves. If you already have a regular breath-practice of some sort – yoga, tai-chi, qui-gong, meditation, mindfulness, or whatever it may be – you will understand how fundamentally good for us breathing out is in itself. If you don't, pre-menstruation would be an excellent time to give yourself a taste – it does not have to be a discipline, and it must not be an effort. Let it be a treat. Any breathing practise is of course also a most excellent preparation for sleep – and good sleep is so very beneficial at this time of the month.

a pause to experience…
Breath meditation for pre-menstruation

It is most important to be as relaxed and comfortable as you can be for this meditation, so make sure you have prepared your sitting or lying place with care. If you can, be in your special west-facing place for this time of the month. And if you can come to this meditation at evening, you will find the mood and feeling of the world around you especially supportive.

the world within women

Let yourself enjoy the nourishing sensation of your in-breaths as you begin to settle. Follow your breath in, so that your attention and attunement gradually move inward to the interior of your body. Spend a little while just experiencing the rise and fall, ebb and flow, of breathing in and out. And then, very gradually let your attention shift more fully to your out-breaths, as they arrive.

Take some time to get acquainted, as much as you possibly can – and then some more – with the **feeling** of breathing out. Extend the time your out-breath takes, little by little, so you can feel it more fully. Allow this to be as pleasurable as possible – long, slow and easy, just following your breath's own flow with no effort at all from you.

As you continue, allow your attention to find any places in your body, mind, heart or soul where there is any holding at all. Now, keeping the pace slow and infinitely gentle, let your out-breaths, one by one, wash through these places of holding. Let any concerns, hurts, worries or fears receive the soft touch of breath, flowing through and around them like a balm. Do not try to 'let them go' – that will put pressure on them and on you. If they are there, they are important, and deserve to be allowed to stay until their messages have been heard and understood. Let your breath reassure each one in turn that you know they are there, and that they have reason to be there – that you are not banishing them, but helping them to know they do not need to hold tight to get your attention. In fact, they can receive more – more awareness, more care, more help – by loosening their grip, letting in the freeing air that is flowing around them. Stay loving and present to your own interior world. Notice what it is like to simply let your out-breath take the pressure off, without having to do any more than that just now. To let your out-breath teach you a different way of carrying things that need your attention.

And in each place you have been attending to, notice what is present when holding has eased. What is there instead, that you could not feel before? Would you like to have more of this in your life? How can you make sure you do receive it – at pre-menstruation and all around your months?

Your out-breath can teach you a *very important art for easing PMT*: the art of un-holding – quite literally of 'no pressure' (what would it be like to really mean this and actually create it inside us every time we say it?). Practise the art of un-holding as much as you can: at all times of the month, at any moment you remember it during your busy days and your nights. When you do notice holding or pressure trying to take care of your worries in the old way, anywhere in your body, thoughts, feelings or sense of yourself – remember this simple and powerful first-aid remedy. Breathe in, and gently breathe out through the place that has tightened. All by itself, it will work wonders.

> The ultimate remedy for PMT **is the art of unholding … 'no pressure'**!

As we go on to examine the femenome's particular teaching-aids for this part of our cycle, we will discover more about the relevance of the out-breath aspect of conscious menstruality.

Personal energy mendala at pre-menstruation

> Conscious menstruality is counter-culture. Culture says *fix it, don't feel it*. Conscious menstruality says *feel it, don't fix it*.
> **Conscious menstruality requires fenomenal courage**

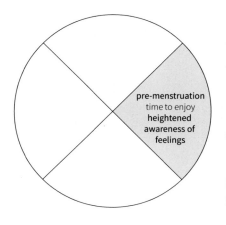

pre-menstruation
time to enjoy
**heightened
awareness of
feelings**

It will come as no surprise at all to learn (or confirm what you already knew) that the teaching module the femenome has in store for us at pre-menstruation is all about our **emotions**! The slowing-down and letting-go lessons of the Nature-mirrors that we studied above are not the primary purpose of the pre-menstrual phase, although they are the essential preliminary to that purpose. Because despite the way Nature slows down or decreases at this point of her

the world within women

cycle, what many of us actually feel is sped up, full up, fed up and ablaze with big feelings, which would seem to be the exact opposite of what the Nature-mirrors are suggesting. So how does this make sense in conscious menstruality?

> Pre-menstruation highlights the faculty of **EMOTIONS**

Have you ever felt that your pre-menstruation comes along and turns your whole life upside down and inside out? If we stop to consider what that familiar phrase actually means, it may indeed be exactly what the femenome intends for us at this time of the month. We might feel as if we have no skin – no buffer zone. That all our innermost feelings and tenderness have been uncovered, exposed, pulled out from their accustomed hiding places, leaving our emotions raw, super-sensitive, maximised, turned outward to a world that bumps and bruises them. That what was most deeply buried is now on top, and the inside of us is on the outside. Women often say they are taken by surprise, or even shocked, at the emotions that erupt in their pre-menstrual days. *Where did that come from,* we ask, as if we had no idea such feelings were in us.

> The femenome asks us to **feel** our life, not think it!

All of these experiences, rough as they can be to go through, are valuable clues for our questions about what is really going on in our menstruality life. Which brings us to something of utmost importance: **the intensified sensations of feeling that we often experience in our pre-menstrual zone** – the rage, tension, mysterious tearfulness; the sense of being wound-up too tightly, the volatility, speedy or depleted energy, nausea, headaches, fatigue, over-wroughtness; the panic and anxiety; the depression and negativity; the edginess, nervy, cranky or manic states; the intolerance, stress and irritability reported to some degree by many, if not most women in this phase – *are not our real feelings, but* reactions, *or* resistance, *to the stirrings of our real feelings.*

> The top layer of intense emotion we often feel at our pre-menstrual time may not be our real feeling (although it is an important clue) **but a *reaction* to the sensation of our real feeling.**

Of course our real feelings **are** big, and **are** intense, because the things that evoke them absolutely **do** matter greatly. But as soon as our menstruality hormones begin to do their work of leading us into our inner world of genuine needs and essential feelings they are going to spark the very question, the hidden longing, that has been contra-culture and implicitly forbidden to women for millennia:

what about ME?

Time and time again, I have seen something in women widen its eyes and recoil from those three small words into a tangle of guilt and fear that if we so much as glance in that direction we will become that thing most abhorrent to the feminine nature:

And so we fall straight into reaction, that familiar tightening of effort and resolve to carry on as best we can *without feeling what we really feel, and without paying attention to what we really need.*

> The pre-menstrual question *what about me?* **is not self-ish.** It is self-inclusive, and therefore necessary and balancing

It really is time for us women to learn a reverse, female version of the Golden Rule we may have been taught as children (do unto others as you would have them do unto you). We could call it the Silver Rule – do unto yourself as you so generously do unto others. Imagine that! What if our loving, nurturing, attentive feminine attributes could be practised *inclusive of ourselves,* taking care of others *as well as,* rather than *instead of,* ourselves!

> The Silver Rule for women: do unto yourself as you so generously do unto others

Here is the reason, simple, loud and clear, why our pre-menstrual emotions and reactions often feel 'over the top'. They feel this way because that is exactly what they are. We are living *over the top of* our real feelings and needs, because we are not supported and do not know how to live *in* them, *with* them and *by* them.

> Pre-menstrual emotions can feel OVER THE TOP because that is exactly what they are. They are the lid over the top of deeper, valid and essential feelings that need our attention

Special features of the pre-menstruation phase

Responding to strong feelings[31]

Our hormones, the teaching tools of the femenome, *want us* to feel more strongly, more sensitively, more deeply, at pre-menstruation. They do stimulate, maybe even provoke, our feeling faculty, because if they did not we would carry on obliviously, in compliance with the edicts of normality, to live from our minds and stay outwardly attuned. Our feelings

---

31   In offering this approach to working with the strong feelings of pre-menstruation I acknowledge with utmost gratitude the teaching of Yasmeen Clark, creator of the Pascha Method of therapy, in which I have been trained and by which I am profoundly influenced. For more information about Pascha Therapy, go to www.pascha.co.nz

are our innermost guidance system, our soul-deep honesty, our paramount source of wisdom. But in a world that prefers to regard emotions as extraneous, distracting and complicating of 'reality', we would have no chance to learn how to handle their largely unexplored potentials unless they insisted on making their presence felt every month in the (sometimes) uncomfortable and (always) un-ignorable ways that they do. Our feelings are here to bring to our attention things that are important to our soul Self and needs that require our response. How do we know what's not-good? What's missing? What needs to change? We **feel** it. As we have already seen (p 132) the femenome is in service to all humanity. It is available to initiate women into a feelings-aware and feelings-inclusive way of life through their menstruality, so that all people can progress by embracing the so-far less developed parts of our human potential.

However, in order to really be available to the femenome's way of bringing us more Self through highlighting our emotions, we need to know how to distinguish our real feelings from the intense, wound-up layer of reactivity that may be sparking off them as we struggle to maintain equilibrium in our feelings-averse world. As we learned from pre-menstruation's Nature-mirrors, this time of the month takes us into a natural **contraction** of energy. Unless we know how to steer ourselves through this shift and arrange our life to support it, we are all too likely to fight its sensations. In our effort to compensate for what feels like a *reduction* in our available energy we become tense in our body and mind, and thus unable to recognise that our energy is actually *interiorising*, not lessening.

The key to navigating this monthly odyssey into our underworld – and the supreme antidote to falling into resistance and unintentionally amping up its challenges – is to *stay open*. Quite an art in itself, given that our most natural and automatic response to things getting difficult is to hold our breath and tighten our body – in other words, get ready to *try harder*.

> The key to navigating pre-menstruation's emotional intensities is to
> ## stay open
> ~~~
> ## Don't try harder – try softer!

the world within women

a pause to consider …
First aid for feelings: the art of staying open

This exercise is designed to follow on from the breath meditation for pre-menstruation given above (p 144). If you haven't already done so, do give yourself plenty of opportunities to practice that one first – it really will help you to move on with this next step.

I would encourage you to play around with this exercise in all sorts of ways – sometimes you may like to work right through it with a feeling that is significant for you. Or it may feel more useful to apply it in parts, according to what you most wish to practice at any particular time, or with different feelings as they arise. Do include practice with enjoyable feelings, as well as those that are more difficult for you to process – these steps will work in the same way for all sorts of feelings.

Staying open is a major part of learning to respond to our feelings, and it will help you not to get stuck in resistance and suffering. It is not the whole process, but the ongoing steps will be able to follow much more easily if you can cultivate this art.

Ensure you are clear in your intention to be open to your pre-menstrual feeling, whatever it may be, not to make it go away, but to understand it better and find a willingness to listen to what it has to tell you. This may not be easy, so just return to the breath meditation above if you feel too full of distress or sensations to be able to settle any deeper.

When you are ready to go a little further, let your breathing fall into a steady, comfortable rhythm, and focus softly on feeling your in-breaths actually creating openings in your body by stretching your ribs and muscles wider, then allowing your out-breaths to maintain that feeling of openness, even as you release the air from your lungs. Keep doing that as you work through the following checklist, or as much of it as you wish to do:

~ can I stay gentle and curious, even when the feeling is intense ~

Am I open physically?

Check for any clenching, constricting, holding or tensing in your body – don't forget your face, jaw and neck, hands and feet. Especially check that your heart is soft, not clenched. Give yourself the time it takes, and the breaths it takes to release any tightness that you find. **Remember, it is the tension you are letting go of, not the feeling itself**. Slowly and lovingly breathe yourself soft and open again. Take down any walls your muscles may have unconsciously built. Relax any combatant postures (we all have them!). Keep your feet on the ground to 'earth' the feeling. Be your own lightening rod. Allow your body to just **experience** your feeling, without having to work with it. Simply keeping breathing for your feeling will give it space and permission to be itself inside you so you can get to know it. Breathe, breathe, breathe – it makes a huge difference, and will support you a lot.

~ Remember: the feeling is not an enemy, it's a messenger ~

Am I open mentally?

Check to make sure you are not unconsciously translating your feelings into thoughts, beliefs or negative interpretations (e.g. 'I'm a failure', 'life is pointless', 'I always...', 'I'll never...'). If you are, take the time to enquire 'What was I **feeling** before those thoughts came in?' Feelings usually have a one-word name – if yours is longer, query it, and open again to the simple name of the **feeling**: (sad, angry, scared, hopeless). Taking care to **name** the feeling accurately and respectfully is a powerful gesture, healing in itself.

Also check whether your mind is busy distracting you from the real feeling – or telling you that you 'shouldn't' be feeling it – or trying to devise ways of stopping feeling it? You are entitled to feel **exactly** what you do feel. Remember, you don't have to work anything out about this feeling. If you can stay open and give it space, it will know what to do.

~ Let your breath help you to feel the feeling, not think it ~

Am I open emotionally?

Are you afraid to let yourself feel your feeling? Check that you are not responding to your feeling with judgement or self-criticism, or pressure to 'solve' it or change it in any way. Is it possible for you to meet this feeling with an open heart, let it in, and let it speak to you? Can you find a willingness to **accept** that this really is how you feel, and how much you feel it? Your feelings always have good reason to exist. They never exaggerate (although our thoughts and interpretations around them can certainly exaggerate). Can you find it in your heart to listen to your feeling as you would listen to a distressed child, or someone you really love? Check your physical heart again to make sure it is still open, as this will help you also keep your emotional heart open. Just take your time with this step if it is difficult. Keep your breathing soft, even if that is all you can do. Can you simply let the sensation of the feeling flow through you without holding it back, and trust it as a sensitive and truthful part of yourself.

~ Feelings are feelings, not failings ~

Am I open spiritually?

Gently check if you are open to what this feeling might ask you to be aware of: how it might want to assist your growth and development? Are you willing to believe the feeling, and not argue with it or try to rationalise it? Can you trust the good intent of your Self and your menstruality, even when you suffer? Are you willing to consider making changes if your menstruality feelings bring distress to your attention? What might the overall purpose, the big picture intention of this feeling be in your life? Do you ask for spiritual help when you need it? Breathe, open, trust, ask.

Consider carefully, what has been the place of your feelings in your life so far? Why does our menstruality insist so strongly that our feelings do get to feature in our life on a monthly basis? Have you noticed that *things matter differently* at your pre-menstrual and menstrual phases than at other times of the month? That the very sensitive and acutely attuned awareness that arises in the pre-menstrual week is much more personal in nature than it was last week? It is as if, through the clear and sharpened eyes of our pre-menstrual and menstrual feelings (and later, even more intensely at menopause) we can see into our inner emotional and spiritual world, where our deepest self-knowledge, desires and needs reside.

a pause to reflect…
Gentling ourselves through mental reactivity

Here are some examples of how we can penetrate the tight clenches that *thoughts about our feelings* can get us into (I have chosen a few of my own old demons that I have really had to learn how to loosen) and how, with care, love and listening, we can open up to the original *feeling* that led to the despairing thought…

What's the point?
becomes
I am longing to feel the point of my life / this experience

What would I love the point to be?

Can I open to seeing myself as a soul capable of such a quest, someone who is yearning to live a meaningful life?

Who *is longing? What deep, loving part of her wants to be included in the meaning of her life?*

I'll never be able to be / do that
becomes
I would so dearly love to find a way to be/do that

What of myself is revealed in my longing to be or do this?

What is it in me that yearns to be expressed, to be fulfilled, in my life in this way?

*What is **her intention** that is cried out in this longing?*

Can I breathe my chest open to this self, so she can have a place to live in my heart even while she is still finding out how to be / do what she wants?

I'm a failure

becomes

There is something I very deeply wish to be, achieve or experience

What is the bud inside me that longs to open up and flower? What is it that my soul so desires to create in this world?

What is not yet supported enough in me for this to be able to come to fruition?

What do I need, so that I do not give up on my purpose?

I hate this

becomes

I truly wanted something other than this

Can I open my heart to what it is that I need, love and long for instead?

What is missing from the balance of my life that would enable me to be all of whom I really am, even when things are difficult? Even when others behave in ways that are not what I want?

How can I keep my compass bearing true to my heart's desires in my present circumstances?

What is the present difficulty illuminating that my soul needs to know?

If we can stay open and attend carefully so that our view is not distorted by reactivity, our awareness during the inner-attuned times of our menstruality might show us things our so-called 'normal life' does not allow us to fulfil or even name. As we realised in our study of hormones earlier in this book, these are often things of a deeply heartfelt or spiritual quality, to do with love, honouring of inner self, being who we truly are in our deepest nature – the most sensitive and sacred aspects of ourselves.

Are these dimensions respected, given space, in the life we are living? If any such feelings are thwarted or unmet, of course there will be sorrow, grief and anxiety in the deep level of Self, who knows they are there. Disallowed pain such as this will manifest as anger, despair, anxiety or depression – and if we have not been allowing ourselves to be aware of our deep inner life, we might wonder where our strong pre-menstrual feelings come from. No matter how accustomed we have become to it over thousands of years, it is not right and not good that our feminine way of being and knowing is given no status in the world. It is not right and not good that our menstruality life has been suppressed. This costs us greatly, and our hormones, knowing our real potential, feel that loss and grief acutely. It is a most justified cause for the anger that erupts in so many of us.

As the femenome's spotlight moves onto the feelings phase of our cycle, it is as if curtains are pulled apart and our inner life is suddenly revealed in all its raw honesty. Everything we have hidden or successfully over-ridden in the more outwardly oriented cycle seasons seizes the opportunity to make its presence felt. In our relationships we are likely to feel acutely issues and irritations we have easily ignored or let go by earlier in the month – and suddenly, to our great puzzlement, they matter a lot and really are unbearable. It is all too easy, when they soften again as our period appears, to write these hormonally amplified surges of intense feeling off, and not believe what they were suggesting. The contrasts in our emotional states at different times of our cycle can be quite dramatic – did we know our spectrum of feeling was *that* wide?

So if our pre-menstrual feelings seem 'over the top', ask what is it they are over the top *of*? If they seem to 'come out of nowhere', our hormones need us to enquire where they *do* come from. If they seem 'out of proportion', what *would* they be in proportion to? Do not allow your strong feelings to be dismissed (by you or anyone else) as 'irrational' or 'unreasonable'. Give yourself permission – once you have breathed your way in past the resistance or reactivity level and found the real feeling at its source – to allow your feeling to be accepted as *true in terms of your inner world. True in the context of your soul's needs, and the life it is longing to live.* It isn't easy to find ways of bringing these strong womanly feelings and needs into a lifestyle that is so accustomed to making no space for them – but it is time to begin. Acknowledging they are there, even if you are not sure what to do with them, is an excellent start. Remember, small steps are enough – in fact, the smallest steps often make the biggest difference in changing how we feel in our lives.

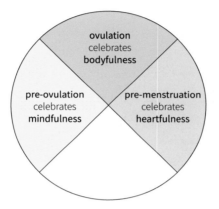

Logical solutions will never work for women because
they leave out whole aspects of our Self

I have often heard women say that they know they should not make any decisions, or try to address relationship issues during their pre-menstrual time – and sad as it is that we have learned to deeply distrust what we feel in this phase, it is also understandable, as the strength and volatility of our pre-menstrual feelings can contrast so strongly with how we see things at other times of our month. However, it is actually most important that we *do* allow our pre-menstrual feelings to have input into our decisions and relationships – not in their raw and reactive state, but in what they reveal to us about those places of deep mattering that our mind can't quite reach. (There will be more about cycle-logical decision-making later, as we look at how the cycle works as a whole in our practical lives. If you'd like a sneak preview of this art see the Kairos Time section starting on p 225).

Remember, our menstruality hormones are working *all around the month.* They don't just pop up out of nowhere at pre-menstruation to make trouble. Isn't it interesting that the hormones of pre-ovulation and ovulation that orient us toward the selfless and other-oriented state of motherhood do not get the bad rap that pre-menstrual hormones do. These favoured hormones are never accused of being 'out of balance', even though they do serve to deaden our sensitivity to our own needs and feelings, and increase our tolerance of things that are hard on us so that we can direct all our energies to those in our care! But we never find fault with them. It does not occur to us that the sudden and apparently aggressive hormonal changes in pre-menstruation could simply be an attempt at adjusting us back to 'normal' or 'balance' from the very outwardly-oriented state that preceded it!

Of course, none of our menstruality states on their own are 'right' or 'balanced'. Balance can only be achieved by including *all* parts of the whole, so that each contributes equally. Our pre-menstrual feelings shout loudly because they have information we need to take into account in our decisions – information we are highly likely to override or contain in the first half of our cycle, in favour of keeping the peace or prioritising others. Our hormones' job is to make sure we don't *avoid* what is essential to our growth and health and happiness. So they *will* do all they can to amp up sensitivity, and, if we let them, consciousness, so that our decisions really can be good for us (and therefore, believe it or not, also good for everyone around us).

> Pre-menstruation is our monthly immersion into heightened sensitivity.
> Heightened sensitivity is the doorway to heightened consciousness

Despair arises when a deep need or desire is unmet. Do not take the despair as the truth about you, but listen carefully to hear the need or desire that wanted to be in your life. That is where the truth lies. Even if you can't see at the moment how it can be met, be open to your desire. It will show you a lot about who you really are. Believing our needs and desires are valid is the first step toward giving them a real place in our life, and only when we can allow this one can the second and following steps gradually reveal themselves.

the world within women

Anger can be volcanic. It arises when feelings are held under pressure until they can no longer be contained. Anger indicates that something matters **a lot.** The risk is that we get tangled in the distress of the anger itself instead of what it actually **is** that matters so much. Breath is the way to take that pressure off safely. Always keep your breathing going, so that you can stay open and let the big sensations of anger move inside you without getting stuck. If you can do this the anger will tell you a whole lot more about what is so very important, and how you need things to be different.

Depression is a disconnection from our Self, and a paralysis of our energy. Like an internal force of gravity, it grinds us to a halt, pulling us down into our deep inner world to see, feel, name and accept what is unhappy there. Depression begs us to know and respond to whatever it is we have avoided, disconnected from, or failed to recognise in our busy outer lives. As we know, when our Self is disconnected it upsets the balance of chemicals and hormones in our body. Do not hesitate to get help (supportive, not suppressant) if you find yourself depressed – it is just too hard to find our way out alone.

It would not be an exaggeration to say that the whole of womankind has been depressed – disconnected and de-energised by having to live at odds with our natural design – for thousands of years. The depression many women experience in their sensitive pre-menstrual state may well be, at least in part, our tapping into that deep collective well of ancient grief and loss. We have not been all that we could be for so long, and deep down, we know it.

Anxiety is also caused by living over the top of unacknowledged feeling. This avoidance tends to produce an array of sensations and symptoms, which may be so intense as to distract us from the original feeling. Our anxiety itself becomes the focus, as the adrenalin it generates, which is meant to help us take action for ourselves, is felt instead as a cause for alarm. We get stuck in our fear response, and it escalates on its own momentum for as long as we continue to avoid the need or feeling that is asking for action. Again, do get help if you suffer from anxiety. We are not meant to be able to unravel its layers on our own.

What might our feelings need from us?

In our conscious menstruality workshops at Luna House we spend some time listening inside ourselves for our feelings to tell us what they actually want from us. Their requests turn out to be touchingly simple and easily achievable. Here are some examples from the lists that women come up with:

- To breathe
- To be heard
- To be accepted
- To be believed
- To be understood (not judged or criticised)
- To be attended to
- To be respected
- To feel supported
- To be fully (and safely) expressed
- For me to show self-love
- For me to be willing to rest if I need to
- For me to be honest about something to myself or someone else
- For me to find the courage to make a change
- For me to ask for help
- For me to take the next step, no matter how small
- For me to let myself matter enough

You might like to write your own list in your menstruality journal, or on a mendala, so your insights will be there to remind you when you next come to your cycle-phase of strong feelings.

What our feelings most need is

TO BE FELT!

a pause to reflect…

What feeling/s does my pre-menstrual phase most regularly bring to me?

What am I afraid to let myself know about my deepest feelings, my inner world, my soul's desires? How can I learn to listen more to these? What would help me to stay connected even in the discomfort of these distressed feelings?

How might my life be different if my deep feelings were allowed to matter more in it?

What help or support might I need to assist me with the important tasks my own personal femenome is presenting to me?

Some bonus apps for pre-menstruation

Sensory magnification

Many women find that it is not only their emotional feelings that are heightened at pre-menstruation, but their five senses as well: seeing, hearing, tasting, smelling and touch sensation (including, for many, an acutely sensitised sexual response). Again, it is as if a buffer zone we didn't even know was there is suddenly whipped away, and we are ultra-sensitive to everything coming toward us. This thin-skinned feeling can be hard to tolerate at times in our bright and blaring world. In psyche-logical terms, though, it invites us to develop the spiritual quality of **heightened perception**. It helps if we can plan our lives as much as possible to avoid pre-menstrual exposure to sensory overloads such as shopping malls, loud music, crowded places, high-volume television (or preferably any television at all) and take ourselves instead to quieter and gentler places where we can learn to enjoy an expanded experience of the world through our opened senses. Who needs perception-enhancing drugs, when we can get the same thing naturally and healthily every single month through our menstruality!

Dis-integration

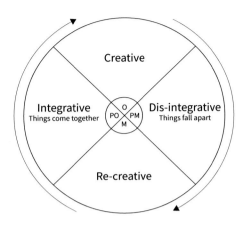

In the femenome's perfect plan for our balance and wholeness, we need to be aware that every part of our cycle will have its opposite energy on the other side of our month.

On the dark side of the moon women often feel that they are stupid, or clumsy – that we are less clear in our thinking, and are behaving in apparently illogical ways. We are not less intelligent – but our intelligence is operating in a different way. We may feel less focussed, because we are so much more open. As we well know, women do multi-channel – and at pre-menstruation and menstruation (and even more so in menopause and cronehood) this talent is amplified.

In our pre-menstrual and menstrual phases we can sometimes feel that *things are falling apart* – and indeed that is exactly what is occurring, physically and energetically. The feeling can be alarming, and we might be tempted to react by trying to *hold it all together, get a grip, keep things under control,* and *pull ourself together:* in other words, to make everything stay the same, rather than surrendering to the energetic change. The more we try or are pressured to do this, the worse we feel, because we are going against our natural flow.

Our capacity for creation must be balanced by our ability to let go, dis-integrate, allow things to end. This is the nature of growth and progression. We need to be able to open our hands, hearts, minds and our bodies, to allow what is no longer required or no longer serving its purpose to flow out of us. There is great wisdom in de-struction, in letting go of what we have known so far. Menstruality will teach us this art. As the femenome takes us, month by month, through the many cycles of our lifelong learning, she is teaching us the womanly art of letting things dis-integrate (come apart) gracefully and elegantly, fearlessly and willingly. What are the parts, now that we can see them separately? What can we learn while they are so distinct – always aware that the next integrating phase of our cycle, when we can put it all back together in a new and better way, is just around

the world within women

the curve? Always remember, open-handed letting go, dis-integrating what has been, are not backward steps, but spiritually progressive and expansive energies – the way to move forward.

Being accident-prone

As a keen mountaineer in my younger life it took me a while to realise that the mysterious fluctuations in my performance on climbs were directly related to where I was in my cycle. At pre-ovulation, and even more at ovulation, I would delight at my strength and prowess, climbing easily and enjoyably up the slopes and ridges, and moving about with balance and agility on wobbly rocks and slippery surfaces. How disappointed I would be, then, only a week or so later, to find that all that wonderful fitness and co-ordination had disappeared. I would struggle grumpily up very similar mountains on shaky and reluctant legs, stopping often to wonder why I pursued a recreation demanding such effort.

Why do women often injure themselves in the pre-menstrual and menstrual phases of their cycle? Partly, this is because they are the two dis-integrative states in our month, as explained above. We will be in every way more vulnerable at these times, and require extra care and awareness. Also, because these feminine states are not properly known and supported in our cultures, we can very easily be misaligned in ourselves, physically and energetically, at these times. We are at odds with our own energy, and therefore less stable and relaxed in our embodiment.

Unfortunately and unfairly, in our unawareness of the physiological changes that require extra consciousness and care, we blindly continue to place *inappropriate demands* on our energy and bodies at these times of our cycle. Just as with electrical wiring, our nervous system has a limit to the amount and type of energy it can supply. If we plug the demand of ovulational energy into the pre-menstrual socket, our system will ping the overload button or else blow a fuse. Our energy is less invested in our physical self at these times, and more concentrated in emotional and spiritual awareness. We need to make allowances for this in the way we move about and the things we expect ourselves to do (especially strenuous demands such as mountain climbing!!). As with everything in conscious menstruality, *awareness is the key.* Do take care.

> Our nervous system is designed by the femenome to provide specialised types of energy at different times of the month. If we plug the demand of ovulational energy into the pre-menstrual socket our system will ping the overload button, or else blow a fuse

Response-ability

Conscious menstruality asks us to really **own** and **trust** our feelings and needs so we don't project them onto others, or let them fly out in distressing or destructive ways. Unfortunately I have noticed that at times women have interpreted my encouragement to allow their heightened emotional state at pre-menstruation as an excuse to be bad-tempered, and expect others to wear it or 'watch out' for it. This is absolutely not a practise of conscious menstruality. The femenome is designed to enable us to grow our own confidence and competence in responding to the feelings our hormones will reveal to us. It is only after we have fully taken response-ability for these intense emotions that we can hope to convey them to anyone else in ways that they will be able to hear.

> If we are reactive to our pre-menstrual feelings and needs others will be reactive to them too. It is **our job** to understand and respond to our feelings and needs so we can effectively convey them to others when appropriate

When we are willing to know, accept and respond to (take response-ability for) our feelings we can be our own lightening rod. It is when our feelings are *ungrounded, and not attached to an awareness that allows us to respond to them*, that they feel out of control and problematic to us. This can undermine our trust in our pre-menstrual feelings and leave us unhappy with ourselves and how we express our emotions.

> Conscious menstruality means taking response-ability for myself

the world within women

Here is a way of developing your response-ability that can help you to feel more deeply what it asks and what it offers in your conscious menstruality practice. This approach is excellent to use at any time of the month, but may be especially revelatory and supportive for you at pre-menstruation and menstruation.

The missing piece in our mothering

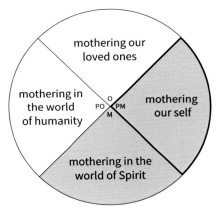

The femenome is always fair and even-handed in her distribution of energies, and this is the case for our mothering inclinations around the month. But the pre-menstrual aspect of our mothering is not one we have been encouraged to develop. When I present this exercise in my workshops at Luna House, women always respond with surprise – it has simply never occurred to most of us that the exquisite and highly honed capacities with which we mother other lives can be available for taking beautiful care of ourselves as well! We have seen the immense difference our love, listening, patience, gentleness, endless forgiveness and seemingly inexhaustible supplies of grace in all its forms makes to our children, our friends, our lover, our communities and our pets – but we have never stopped to consider how beneficial these very same attributes might be to ourselves when we are weary, broken-hearted, worn down, afraid or grief-stricken.

> On the dark side of the moon the femenome is asking us to be **our own mother**

A little mothering goes a long way any time of the month, but when we are tired, stretched, or pitched into the highly sensitive states of pre-menstruation, it can be a most necessary and effective balm to soothe and settle anything that is disturbed inside us. Mother-love is a unique and potent energy in the world – there is truly nothing else quite so beneficent, persevering and generous. We (quite rightly) never outgrow our need for its wise and compassionate ministrations, and it just might be time to check whether we have somehow assumed we should be able to do without it once we are mothers or 'grown-ups' ourselves. The deep care and unconditionality of mother-love, being the exact opposite of the harsh and self-critical states we can fall into at pre-menstruation, make it the ultimate remedy for these times of heightened vulnerability.

a pause to experience...
Being our own mother

Take some time to list all the qualities of a good mother that you are aware of in the ways you have responded to your children, or others you have loved in your life (e.g. patience, love, gentleness, care, warmth, understanding, compassion, empathy, non-judgment, acceptance...)

Include also qualities you have seen and appreciated in other mothers. If your own mother was a good mother, write down what made her so, and how her mother-qualities made you feel as you received them. Or consider grand-mothers you have known, and how they love.

And if the mother you had was not able to mother well, write down what you wish she could have given you, and the difference it would have made if you had got it.

Make your list as full as you can, and write or draw it in your menstruality journal, where you can see it. Allow yourself to reflect on these and where they come from within you and other women. Take time to enjoy their presence inside you and their good effect in the world. How have you seen your loved ones benefitting from your mother-qualities?

Then choose one feeling that is strong, repetitive or troubling for you in your menstruality. Write/draw/describe/symbolise it in your journal.

Now take some time to connect to the **feeling** of the mother qualities you listed above. Choose one or two in particular that you know you are good at. Wait until you can feel the sensation of them in your body. Let your heart fill with the presence of the mother you know you can be.

How would this mother respond to the menstruality feeling you have identified as not easy for you? Write/draw/symbolise her response in your journal.

Attune to the sensation of what it is like for your menstruality feeling to receive this kind of response. What difference does it make? What becomes possible because of it?

What would it be like to know that your distressed feelings can always turn to this source of motherly support?

The greatest gift of the femenome to us in our pre-menstrual apprenticeship is the confidence to respond to our own strong emotions, so that we become free (from reactivity in ourselves and others) to engage in the huge and wondrous resource of our true feelings, and all the richness they can make available to us on our life path. Our feelings are a goldmine of soul-energy that will quite amazingly enhance our sense of self and the opportunities life can hold for us. Pre-menstruation, notorious for being the most challenging of the menstrual cycle quarters, is equivalently rewarding. It is not for nothing that the femenome provides us with up to 500 cycles in which we can gradually become adept in the boundless possibilities of living by our feelings.

The more consciously we embrace each pre-menstrual time, the more prepared we will be to graduate into the big feeling capacities of our menopause when that time comes.
Bon voyage!!

x

at a glance...

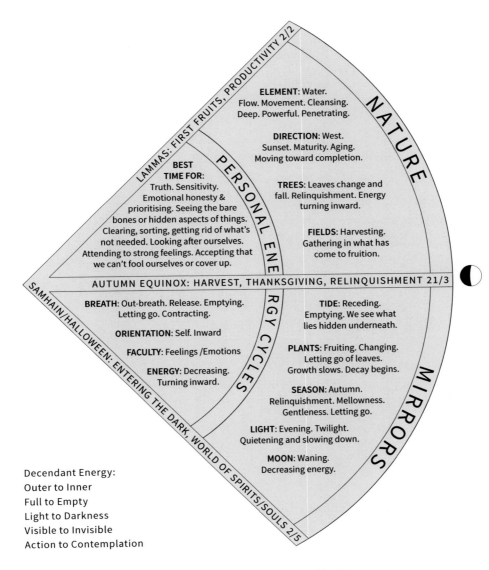

ELEMENT: Water.
Flow. Movement. Cleansing.
Deep. Powerful. Penetrating.

DIRECTION: West.
Sunset. Maturity. Aging.
Moving toward completion.

TREES: Leaves change and
fall. Relinquishment. Energy
turning inward.

FIELDS: Harvesting.
Gathering in what has
come to fruition.

BEST TIME FOR:
Truth. Sensitivity.
Emotional honesty &
prioritising. Seeing the bare
bones or hidden aspects of things.
Clearing, sorting, getting rid of what's
not needed. Looking after ourselves.
Attending to strong feelings. Accepting that
we can't fool ourselves or cover up.

NATURE

PERSONAL ENERGY CYCLES

MIRRORS

LAMMAS: FIRST FRUITS, PRODUCTIVITY 2/2

AUTUMN EQUINOX: HARVEST, THANKSGIVING, RELINQUISHMENT 21/3

SAMHAIN/HALLOWEEN: ENTERING THE DARK, WORLD OF SPIRITS/SOULS 2/5

BREATH: Out-breath. Release. Emptying.
Letting go. Contracting.

ORIENTATION: Self. Inward

FACULTY: Feelings /Emotions

ENERGY: Decreasing.
Turning inward.

TIDE: Receding.
Emptying. We see what
lies hidden underneath.

PLANTS: Fruiting. Changing.
Letting go of leaves.
Growth slows. Decay begins.

SEASON: Autumn.
Relinquishment. Mellowness.
Gentleness. Letting go.

LIGHT: Evening. Twilight.
Quietening and slowing down.

MOON: Waning.
Decreasing energy.

Decendant Energy:
Outer to Inner
Full to Empty
Light to Darkness
Visible to Invisible
Action to Contemplation

Pre-Menstruation Phase Chart

Energy of re-creation, integration, and completion

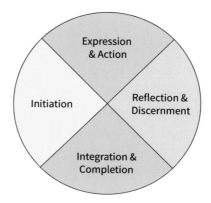

As I was preparing to write this chapter I came across the following long-forgotten entry in my own journal. My friend Penelope was staying with me at Luna House, just on the cusp of her pre-menstrual and menstrual phases. What better way can there be to describe the femenome than simple observations of how it makes its presence felt in a woman's ordinary life?

… We go out to our class in the evening, and I observe how open she is – experiencing her own and others' states intensely and feeling acute and ultra-sensitive emotional responses to what is occurring within and around her. She is clearly very open and connected to the extra-sensory world as well, to spiritual and interior realms.

Next morning she tells me that her bleeding has begun in the night, and this makes sense of her intense response the evening before. She is moving slowly, sitting dreamily, slipping into reverie at the breakfast table… she had not been willing to come out of her sleep, and does not feel like going to work.

While we are eating breakfast she tells me one of two dreams from her night: She is driving a huge, heavy truck-trailer, loaded with rocks. Although she enjoys the view of the world she gets from up in the truck's cab, she is anxious, not confident that she can handle driving this thing. She feels that **this is not woman's work.**

After telling her dream she slips into reverie again, so that when I ask for the second dream she does not hear me, or answer. I see her body inclining forward, as if to enter deeply into her inner world, folding over on herself. And I see that her energy is very inward – even though she knows it is getting late and she must drive into the city to work, she moves slowly, dreamily…

Brushing her teeth at the window she feels the sun on her face, and accepts that she is not going to go to work – that there is something other, bigger, much more important for her to attend to. She will dedicate her day instead to menstruation – to the universally present, but long unpractised feminine art of 'walking between the worlds'. Her dream has told her that the worldly labour expected of her is indeed not woman's work at this time of her month. She does not feel confident or right doing that. Woman's work now is to be open to the part of our potential not usually included or asked for in day-to-day human awareness, but **crucial** *to life itself, as all the Nature-mirrors show us.*

In her open, dreamy state, if she can allow it, she will meditate, day-dream, perhaps even sleep. She can slow to a complete stop, so that there is emptiness and stillness, quiet space inside her to listen into. And because of that, she will be wide open to prompts, inspirations, guidance – from her own soul, from intuition, from silence, from darkness, from her unobstructed receptivity to Nature, spirit, the universe, the divine – whatever we may like to call that bigger picture we all know and long to feel. She will see things in a different light, quite literally, and be capable of insights (in-sights) and perspectives that are more spiritual, and therefore from a wider frame of reference, than at any other time of the month. Through her opened birthing-body she is drawing more Self, more soul, more consciousness into the world. O yes, she does have woman's work to do today …

Fenomenology 204, menstruation, is the completing phase of our monthly traverse around the whole spectrum of our nature. 'Complete' has two meanings – to finish, but also to make whole, to include all parts. Remembering that the potter's wheel spun by the hand of the femenome through all our years of cycling is the mendala, let's take a closer psyche-logical and cycle-logical look at our symbol:

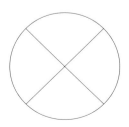

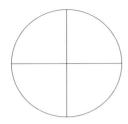

The mendala is closely related to an ancient symbol for Earth, the ultimate mother and container of all that exists. We can also easily see that both the mendala and the Earth symbol are made by putting together the 2 elements of the Venus symbol that we all know represents us as women. The cross was symbolic of women in their sacred relationship to the fourfold natural world long before it became a masculine and Christian figure. However it may be only now, as we are moving forward from the threefold and into the fourfold understanding of the feminine design that we can fully feel its significance to us. As women reclaim the cross as their symbol of incorporating the four quarters that make up a whole, we can see that our design is, quite literally, **crucial** (in the form of a cross). It is perhaps more than a happy coincidence that the English language makes the very same word an apt reminder for us that we women, because of the form of our mendala, are **crucial** (essential, necessary and of great value) to human wellbeing, healing and progress – because we are learning, month by month and throughout our lives, to embody the Laws of Nature and the principles of all life.

In our dangerously out-of-balance 21st century world, the masculine is searching, consciously and unconsciously, for the feminine element he lacks and longs for. This is not to be found in what he already has – or in what we have tried to prove we are good at – but in what is *different* about us: our prowess in the two least developed faculties of humanity, emotions and spirituality. Little wonder that these are the two quadrants of the mendala most provoked by the femenome.

What will this mean for us in the menstruation season of our cycle?

Nature-mirrors at menstruation

And don't think the garden
loses its ecstasy in winter.
It's quiet, but
the roots are down there riotous

Rumi

At menstruation, in synch with all the rhythms of Nature, we are engaging with energy that is *inward*. At this time of her month a woman will usually feel that she has little energy for activity or outer demands. She craves quiet time for herself alone, and if she could she would retreat from all her accustomed tasks and responsibilities. She doesn't want to have to think, perform or provide, and wishes just to rest. This makes perfect sense when we consider the many reflections of this state in Nature. The moon is absent from our night sky, its light apparently extinguished. The tide is fully out – ebbed away to emptiness. Trees have lost their leaves and stand bare. Winter strips colour, light and warmth from the landscape, and all seems still and quiet.

What has happened to the vitality of life? Birds and animals are asleep or even hibernating. Fields are bare and little food can be found above ground. Nothing is flowering or growing, and any unharvested fruits and berries have fallen and rotted. Nature appears almost to have closed down. How much space and attention do we give our own pause, our interiorised menstrual life, to make sure it has as much vitality as our outer, worldly life? Are *our* roots down there riotous? What *are* our roots? How do we nourish them?

The turning inward of our energy may leave our outer life apparently weary, de-energised, or 'down'. This, though, far from being a loss of energy, is a re-investment of it in the inner, invisible life. A tree without leaves has not died. Though it may stand devoid of any *sign* of life on a winter's night, inside its trunk and roots life is surging. It's not so easy to attend to external and internal work in our lives simultaneously so the femenome kindly ensures we can do each in turn, in the beautifully balanced oscillation of our cycle around its monthly axis.

> A bare winter tree is not dead. It has **interiorised** its energy as we do at menstruation

At the very heart of our menstrual mendala quadrant stands a triple darkness: mid-night, mid-winter and the mid-point of the dark moon phase.

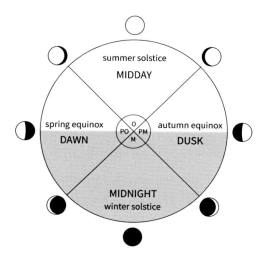

Here is the powerful realm of darkness inside us – the fertile void of nothingness, emptiness, stillness. The point between ending and beginning. The moment-ous moment of suspended moment-um in all of the rhythms of life. The place of potency and potential where nothing is (apparently) happening and everything is re-creating itself. This is the fulcrum, the balance-point, *the still point of the turning world*[32], the hinge between ending and beginning which holds the key to life's continuance.

At menstruation (for us in the southern hemisphere) the compass-bearing of our mendala points directly **south**. South is cool, silent, beneath, hidden. In contrast to the fiery, active and moving energy of our north, south is still, even fixed – the **direction** in which the longitudinal lines of Earth's sphere are contracting, and will eventually converge into their source and destination. South is home-base, the place where each pulsation of life's cycles begins and ends. It is Earth's amen to the prayer of the cycle just lived; the place where a full stop goes at the end of a sentence; the final chord of resolution in a piece of music.

Our **element** mirror at menstruation is earth. **Earth** is the *foundation* of life – its point of reference, nourisher and sustainer. Menstruation, like the roots of a tree or the keel of a boat, has a *grounding* and *stabilising* effect on our monthly energy. It *earths* us, pulling us back into connection with our source and guiding forces, and re-aligning us with our soul's

---

32   TS Eliot, in his wonderful poem *Four Quartets*, dives deeply and eloquently into this mystical moment, and names it *the still point of the turning world*

the world within women

purpose. Earth, too, is quite literally our home-base, both womb and tomb, the beginning and ending of all terrestrial forms of life. Like home, it's where we come and go from, plug ourselves in to recharge our batteries, renewing our energy for our next cycle of life. It is not for nothing that the feelings of menstruation make us want to go-to-ground: sit still or lie down, be inward, meditate, contemplate, rest and re-attune to our inner self. To help us steer our life's boat through all the currents and cross-currents of the world, menstruation will check our co-ordinates and adjust the rudder underneath us to make sure we are on course.

The mirror-image of menstruation in the life-cycle of plants is the **seed**. Just as in the age-old riddle of the chicken and the egg, who could ever say whether the seed is the first stage or the last stage of a plant's life? In the exquisite and paradoxical nature of life itself, it is both. The seed is the alpha and the omega[33], the beginning and end phase both at once, of plant cycles.

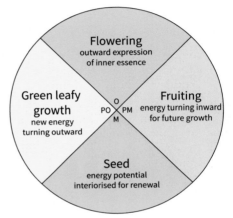

And there is another magic of happy co-incidence here for us to contemplate. If we write the word omega differently, with the mega inside the O, it will show us a further and very sacred way in which the seed is a Nature-mirror for our menstrual state: something huge contained in something tiny. Just as a massive oak tree resides within a little acorn, the femenome wants to remind us that inside the small circle of our human self we are actually mega beings, extra-ordinary (beyond-ordinary) souls

living ordinary lives. As we continue in our exploration of menstruation we will see that one of the special reminders of this part of our cycle is that our inner world is bigger than our outer world. Daring to dive into the apparent nothingness of that O we find both eternity and infinity!

---

33   If you are not already familiar with these words, they are the first and last letters of the Greek alphabet, and often used to describe beginning and end in a profound or overall sense

In the seed phase, the whole of a plant's nature, life and potential becomes self-contained, not needing to receive anything from the world around it until it is ready to commence a new cycle. All is within, and what is within is absolutely sufficient. A seed, though it lies still in the dark and looks lifeless, is full of vitality. Everything that plant experienced in its *outer* phase – all that it received of the four elements of air, sunlight, water and earth to sustain its life in the world – is now contained *inside* its tiny form, suspended in potential, **integrated** into a new manifestation of itself.

Seeds are the supreme teachers of the two main lessons of our menstrual phase: interiority and the art of the pause. Plants know what humans have forgotten – that all growth, all wellbeing, all maturation must go through phases of contraction and pause to balance its expansions if it is to reach its full potential. If you are not sure how this works, just tune in to your breath cycle once again for a moment, and see what it is like to start your next in-breath immediately after your out-breath, without leaving a pause. Keep that going for a few breaths, and you will soon feel how it starts to upset the whole cycle – how distressing and unsustainable it is. (If only our economists realised that a concept of 'growth' that does not include contractions and pauses is doomed to self-destruct!)

Menstruation in the holographic femenome

Winter solstice, midnight, dark moon, ebbtide, the central points of our menstrual phase, are emblematic of cronehood in the holographic femenome.

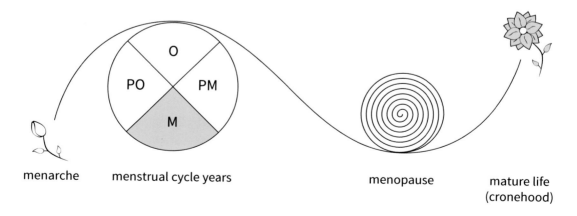

menarche   menstrual cycle years   menopause   mature life
                                                                          (cronehood)

Do we regard cronehood as a decline, something to fear or dread in its nearness to death? Let me tell you, as someone now embarking on that fourth phase of the femenome, the path has never felt wider or brighter under my feet and the nearness of death just means I get to feel and see the magnificent expansiveness of Heaven while still living on Earth. What is more, that Heaven is inside me, not beyond me! The monthly taste of cronehood that the femenome brings to us at menstruation is offered as a sip from the cup containing the Elixir of Life – the most wondrous secrets that we are all allowed to access by following the prompts to turn inward at this time of our cycle.

> At menstruation the femenome invites us to know that the world inside us is bigger than the world around us

The more you can arrange your life to let in the glorious gifts of your little cronehood at each menstruation phase of your cycle, the readier you will be, when you eventually complete your menopause, to enter the magnify-cent world of big cronehood and taste the bliss that awaits you there.

The Celtic festival that ushers in the menstruation phase of our mendala is one that can help us in a particular way to be more aware of the special nature of this part of our cycle.

Samhain, otherwise known as Hallowe'en, has unfortunately been commercialised and is celebrated at the wrong time of the year (spring) in the southern hemisphere. As the name Hallow E'en suggests, this festival is the eve of a holy season, the moment of entering the darkest quarter of the year. In Celtic lore this is known as the Dark, the realm of death, of souls, or the Otherworld, the abode of spirit. It is an autumn and an evening festival. The Celts' ways of celebrating included specifically making room in their lives for the reality of death, for example setting a place at their table on that day for departed family members to join them at meals. In this worldview death is not the end of life, but the other, unseen aspect of it that is always with us even when we prefer to pretend it is not. The reality is that we step quite happily, even eagerly, into this Otherworld – this mystical darkness, the realm of our own soul's life, separate from and unknown to our day-mind – every night when we go to sleep.

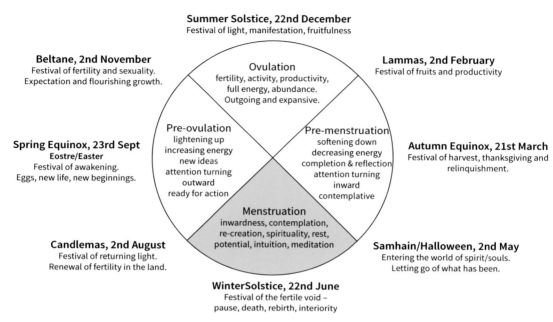

Summer Solstice, 22nd December
Festival of light, manifestation, fruitfulness

Beltane, 2nd November
Festival of fertility and sexuality.
Expectation and flourishing growth.

Lammas, 2nd February
Festival of fruits and productivity

Ovulation
fertility, activity, productivity,
full energy, abundance.
Outgoing and expansive.

Pre-ovulation
lightening up
increasing energy
new ideas
attention turning
outward
ready for action

Pre-menstruation
softening down
decreasing energy
completion & reflection
attention turning
inward
contemplative

Spring Equinox, 23rd Sept
Eostre/Easter
Festival of awakening.
Eggs, new life, new beginnings.

Autumn Equinox, 21st March
Festival of harvest, thanksgiving and
relinquishment.

Menstruation
inwardness, contemplation,
re-creation, spirituality, rest,
potential, intuition, meditation

Candlemas, 2nd August
Festival of returning light.
Renewal of fertility in the land.

Samhain/Halloween, 2nd May
Entering the world of spirit/souls.
Letting go of what has been.

WinterSolstice, 22nd June
Festival of the fertile void –
pause, death, rebirth, interiority

Seasonal festival Nature-mirror for menstruation (southern hemisphere)

In conscious menstruality we have no need to take ourselves back to earlier times or customs. Living according to the femenome does not ask for rituals or rites, although some women do like to include them and they can be very enjoyable and helpful to connect us to the feminine in ourselves and others. However, they are not enough on their own. The femenome teaches simply and directly by experience in our here-and-now life – you have to be there! How can we align to what ebbs and flows inside us, so that our inner seasonal changes are not just symbolic celebrations but applied to a daily and practical way of life in which we can thrive? If we are to receive the benefits of living according to our cycle, they have to be experienced physically, in our body. As we already know, the very best way to 'get the feel of' the femenome living inside us is through the awareness-doorway opened by our breath.

the world within women

a pause to experience ...
Breath meditation for menstruation

[If you do not menstruate for any reason, you will still find this exercise most beneficial. You may like to do it during the dark moon phase each month.]

Make sure you are as comfortable as you possibly can be for this meditation, and that you have everything you need to stay warm and supported for as long as you want to spend. (If you have pain or discomfort with your bleeding, there will be another exercise for you a little further on in this chapter.) Darkness and silence will be ideal, but any conditions you prefer and can manage will be fine. Arrange your body in a way that allows a sense of openness and flow throughout, especially in your pelvic and vaginal areas, and also along the insides of your thighs. Take some time now for each slow in-breath to assist opening in every part of your body, especially any that might feel inclined to hold. Pay special attention to your belly – is it soft? Moving in and out with your breath? Can it be even softer? If it is tender or uncomfortable, let your breath be like the ministering hands of a most loving healer or female guide inside you, someone who totally understands that discomfort, and knows just what is needed to ease it.

Now start to tune in to the rhythm of your breath, allowing its pace to be exactly as is most comfortable for you today. Notice the long, drawing-in and releasing-out phases – and also the short little pauses at the top and bottom of your breath cycle. And then let your awareness float down naturally and easily into your body on your next out-breath so that you can fully experience the pause of emptiness there. Without straining your breath in any way, or trying to make the pause between breaths longer, begin to notice what that tiny interlude is like for you.

Feel the sensation of emptiness. There is nothing here now except you, your own interior world. How big is it, now that you are there? Who are you, when there is nothing for you to be full of or busy with. Stay connected to your interior world, once you can feel it, as your breaths continue to rise and fall. Now you may be ready to extend that pause just a little, but not in any way that is an effort, or uncomfortable. Just as a place to sink into. Relax as deeply as you can into the pause, brief as it is, and feel what it puts you in touch with. It may feel like a glimpse between curtains, or through a door just slightly ajar. It is true that menstruation takes us to a doorway, and it is important to get to know, and trust, this sensation of being at a threshold **that is inside you!** Take care not to let your mind imagine what might be through the doorway – that will only take you somewhere else.

If what you meet in this inner place is sad, hurting, afraid or in any way distressed, take yourself back to the exercises for pre-menstruation, and be the loving mother that this vulnerable part of you needs.

If you feel sleepy, sleep. Emptiness and effortlessness are not very familiar places for some of us to go. If you can easily stay awake, just listen in to those tiny but vast pauses. In the silence and stillness of no effort, what do you hear? Whose presence is it that you feel when there is nothing to distract you? What do you sense, know and trust on this threshold? Keep reassuring your mind that it is not yet her turn – there is nothing she needs to interpret here. Just rest in all that is there for you in the sweet ease of nothingness.

Later, you might like to draw, write, dance or symbolise your threshold place – the unique, innerworld crossing place that exists only in you.

Here is a mini meditation you can do in any breath-cycle (making sure you give equal time and receptivity to each phase) – or on a daily basis, with a brief visit at morning, midday, evening and night – or indeed on a monthly basis, at each quarter of your cycle. You will also find of course that it mirrors the seasons of the year perfectly. Feel the multiple mirrors within this simple shape, and know that in connecting with it you are touching into the sweet and simple pulse-beat of life itself, the rhythm that keeps our planet and everything on it turning. Feel yourself a part of all that, and relax, knowing you are held by layers upon layers of the holograph of life.

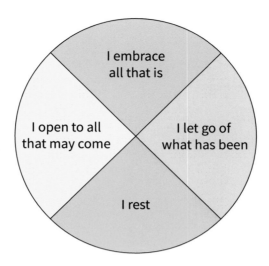

Personal energy mendala at menstruation

Menstruation highlights the faculty of **SOUL/SPIRITUALITY**

menstruation
time to enjoy
the spiritual dimension
of who we are

In our daily rhythm, night is the time when we sleep, just as Nature does in winter. A bare winter tree is not dead – as Rumi says, it is ecstatic on the inside, its underground and interior parts humming with life. In the same way, a sleeping person is not **un**conscious, but **otherly**-conscious – visiting the vast realms of their dream life and spiritual reality. At menstruation we are invited to immerse ourselves in our often unrecognised fourth faculty, the **spiritual** dimension of our nature. To get there we have to leave our ordinary, rational state behind – release ourselves from its scope and go beyond the limits it knows. Why are we women often slow and dreamy in our menstrual time? Why do we want to be resting or sleeping? The femenome is inducting us into the mystical part of our nature, teaching us quite literally to walk between the worlds. It is women's most special and sacred prerogative at menstruation to open the door between the ordinary world of daytime living, and the ir-rational (beyond-rational) world we can usually only access in sleep, and to live with one foot in each! This is no small thing to accomplish, which is why, in times past, women would withdraw from the ordinary demands of life to do it.

> It is the menstrual phase of our cycle (our monthly mini-cronehood) that takes us into the bigger dimensions of who we really are – the place we could otherwise only access in sleep

a pause to consider...

Everyone is spiritual by nature. Our spirituality is unique and personal to us. For some of us it might be a sense of deep connection with Nature; for others a more formal belief, perhaps shared with companions of the same outlook, or best experienced in solitude. Some of us will have practices which express or nourish our spirituality. And some will prefer to connect with their spiritual aspects in simple and spontaneous ways. What is important, and especially enjoyable at our menstrual time, is to value this part of our nature and ensure we make time for it. Journalling is a particularly good way to get to know your spiritual life – it just might surprise you if you really open up to it. Here are some questions you may like to explore in your menstruality journal. I would also encourage you, as your time allows, to record your spiritual states and experiences around the month on a special mendala you can make for that purpose:

What is my spirituality?

How do I define and describe it to myself? What would it look like if I drew/painted it? What would it feel like if I danced it? How would it sound if I heard it? What would its fragrance be if I smelled it? Its texture if I touched it?

How important is it to me?

What part does it play in my ordinary life?

How much time do I allow this part of myself in my busy life? Is it enough? If not, what could I do to create more space for it? (make these steps small, enjoyable and manageable for yourself)

How would I like to enjoy my spiritual self more?

What feeds, nourishes, inspires me spiritually? Dancing, reading, meditation, time in Nature? Beauty? Art? Prayer? Creativity? Music? Play? Poetry? What else?

How much of that do I get regularly? Is it enough? If not, how can I let it matter enough to get more?

We know from all our Nature-mirrors that menstruation is the phase of energetic *withdrawal* in our cycle. However, it is most important to re-cognise (know differently) that this is not a withdrawal *from* the world, so much as a withdrawal *into* a very special place – the Otherworld of our own inner soul-space where everything is alive and vibrant, and the roots are riotous because they remember their divine origins. It is a withdrawal into interiority, not oblivion – a very active and conscious state, not to be confused with passivity or disconnection from ourself. We are closed to be open, withdrawn to be connected. It is in fact a deeply receptive state, but its receptivity is attuned to our Self's own deep sources, the unconscious and intuitive treasuries within. In this way it is opposite and complementary to the other-attuned receptivity of ovulation.

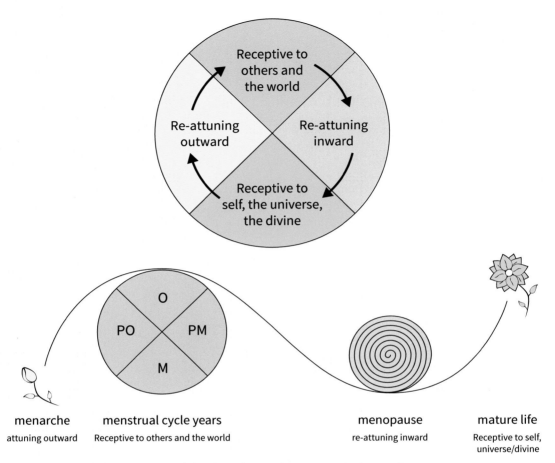

Receptivity flow in the femenome holograph

a pause to reflect ...

It is of utmost importance now, as we begin to recover knowledge of our cycle, that we honour and appreciate the ways in which we *have* managed to continue as best we can to live in its profound variations of energy with no acknowledgement of what we are doing.

For women who are not cycling or not menstruating, you can engage in this exercise fully knowing that the very same spiritual qualities and doorways are available and can be sought inside you, even though not made evident or highlighted by monthly bleeding.

Imagine for a moment the difference it would make to your life if you were **allowed**, **expected** and **supported** to have some undisturbed time in your interior, spiritual, intuitive world every month while bleeding. What would you like to do with that time?

How much, and in what ways, do you trust your interior/spiritual life as a reference point for your own outer life in the world? Take time to identify these as clearly as you can, and write them down in your menstruality journal. What do you turn to, or consult, within yourself, and how do you do that? Even if you are not accustomed to thinking of yourself in this way, pay attention to **your** *way of connecting with your bigger-picture world…*

How much, and in what ways, do you trust your interior/spiritual/menstrual life to be able to contribute meaningfully to the lives of others around you? To your relationships: intimate? Family? Social? Write these down too, as you realise them. Be as specific and detailed as you can.

How much, and in what ways, do you trust your interior/spiritual/menstrual life to make you a contributing member of your community? Of humanity in general? What would you **like** *it to contribute if you dared to believe that those offerings would be accepted? Be courageous, and write down everything you truly wish. It is most important that you acknowledge to yourself who you really want to be in the world – because that* **is** *who you truly are!*

In Ancient Greece menstruating women were revered as prophets, and their advice was sought in all political matters. At your next Menstruation, making sure you are deeply and trustingly connected to your beyond-rational place inside, write down the advice you would give community and world leaders, or anyone who occurs to you. Let yourself write just what comes, exactly as it comes. Keep your list, and look at it later in your month. How does your unedited menstrual knowledge feel to you at each subsequent phase of your cycle?

What might the world be like
if all its women were bringing a spiritual or intuitive element
into the decisions and directions humanity takes?
We have what it takes to heal and change our world, and bring it back into
balance.

For women who experience menstrual pain

We are not designed to suffer with our periods, and the fact that so many women do should be heard as a big and loud wake-up call that something is very wrong for femaleness in this world. So, as we discussed earlier in this book, the very first reassurance to breathe into your body if you do experience pain or discomfort with your bleeding is that **this is not your fault.** It is not something that is wrong **with** you, but something that is very wrong **for** you.

> Menstrual pain is not caused by menstruation. Menstrual pain is not caused by being female. Menstrual pain is caused by internalised cultural resistance and environmental toxicity. MENSTRUAL PAIN IS A WARNING THAT URGENTLY NEEDS TO BE TAKEN SERIOUSLY

We are deeply conditioned to respond to pain by trying to get rid of it as quickly as we can, so we can resume living a 'normal' life and doing what is expected of us. Unfortunately this is precisely the kind of habitual resistance that will make our menstruality call out more loudly from inside us, trying to alert our attention to what it needs us to be conscious of. It is not at all easy to respond to pain and discomfort in a different way – we instinctively want our awareness to get away from where the pain is, rather than going toward it. So you will need to bring all of the qualities you identified in the 'Being our own mother' exercise forward with you into your menstrual week.

Menstrual pain is not caused by menstruation – it is caused by things around and within us that are bad for us. Our environment is soaked in toxicity, and much of that, sadly, is personally unavoidable until there is enough political consciousness to stop loading our air, water and food with poisons. What we can to some degree choose, is to eat organically, and this is absolutely essential to our menstruality health, as many of the chemicals routinely sprayed on our food are known hormone-disruptors. Do your very best to avoid as much as you possibly can the pollutants that drench our world. Do remember that ever-increasing bombardments of radiation from our numerous electronic devices is another major contributor to the stress our hormones are under, and ensure you do not have any devices with screens in the room where you sleep. Get as much fresh air and clean water as you possibly can. The 'unimproved' life-supports provided by our mother Earth really are the very best medicines available.

> The pesticides, herbicides and artificial hormones routinely sprayed on our food ARE toxic to humans and DO harm our hormones. They are a major contributor to menstrual pain. As much as you possibly can, let yourself matter enough to grow and buy organic food.

As we have seen earlier any resistance at all in our body will add to the likelihood of menstrual pain for us. It is virtually impossible to menstruate without resistance in an environment that makes no allowance for it, and in fact requires us to override almost everything about our femaleness. Where menstruation itself is felt as an unwelcome intrusion, our muscles cannot be fully relaxed. Body tension creates dams against our menstrual energy flow, and pain is the result.

Remember, our finely-tuned hormonal secretions are directly affected by our ability to respond, or not, to how we are feeling. The toxicity-loading of our system will determine how freely and effectively conscious energy can or cannot flow along the neural pathways of our body. Where consciousness is not present, pain is all there is. Its intense sensations get to take up our entire inner space and can easily become overwhelming if no Self is alongside to keep our system open.

> Where consciousness and care are not present pain is **all** there is. An attentive and responsive Self inside us can change our pain experience immensely.

Our job, just as with the uncomfortable emotional feelings of pre-menstruation, is to learn how to *respond* rather than *reacting* to any pain we may encounter. And that takes a very fine-tuned awareness of exactly what and how we are resisting. It is reassuring to know that all of our care and practice in responding to our pre-menstrual feelings will greatly assist in reducing menstrual pain as well, as we will come in to our bleeding time with much less stored tension, emotion and stress.

Let's remember, femaleness itself has been resisted, disparaged and unfavoured for thousands of years. It's hard to feel reverence toward our menstruating body, or create conditions that will optimise her experience when everything around you says it's inconvenient, inferior and undesirable – or, in our supposedly advanced times, *redundant*. How many women do you know who take a few days off every month to menstruate? The sheer impossibility of doing so is all the evidence we need of how massively femaleness is disallowed in our times.

> If we 'haven't got time to sit around menstruating' our menstruation will have to find other voices to let us know she is there!

Menstrual pain is very intense for some women (our sensitive canaries) and felt to some degree by most of us. It has a very compelling quality to it, pulling and tugging at us, gathering in the lower part of our abdomen and back, drawing down sometimes really heavily – as if it is trying to pull our whole being down through our birth canal. Some women feel an immense heaviness, a flow-down, slow-down inwardness. One of the functions of pain is that it draws us very intensely to focus on its sensations and locations. When

the world within women

we allow ourselves to fully feel the powerful bearing-down sensations of menstruation, it could almost be the bodily experience of giving birth to ourselves. Menstruation can feel like a concentrated, internal force of gravity, pulling all of our attention into our own birthing organs, as if to refuse to allow us to distract ourselves from this important process by focussing on worldly tasks. Really, when we stop and listen, it is quite clear and explicit in its requests of us – the sensations say it all. The only mystery is why we are mystified by such a clear message. What if menstrual pain wants us to just stop and menstruate!

> Menstrual pain really wants us to STOP and
> MENSTRUATE instead of carrying on regardless

Do we ever stop to wonder what the verb *menstruate* would mean if we decided to make it a known and allowed and respected action? How would you **like** to menstruate? What would your menstrual pain like to suggest to you about how it could best be done? Pay close attention to its prompts! They are very important information.

> What would the verb 'menstruate' mean if it was a valued and
> respected activity in our communities? How would we like to
> menstruate, if we could choose and design our own conditions?

a pause to consider ...
Responding to our menstrual pain

Bring your menstruality journal or mendala to a soft, warm, quiet and comfortable place that you have prepared in advance for your menstruation. Make sure everything is there to help you feel acknowledged, honoured and cared-for as a menstruating woman.

First of all, take all the time you need to find inside you your own mother from the exercise on p 166, and bring her with you into your menstruating place. Breathe her in, so that you feel her taking charge of looking after you. How does she respond to knowing you are in pain?

Now allow your breath to very gently visit every part of your body and discover where there is holding or tension. Let your pain guide you with this. Breathe your attention inward, gently, to where the pain is strongest. Do not be dismayed if you find this hard to do – it **is** hard to do.

For a moment, just allow the experience of your breath taking your motherly awareness and care **to** the pain, instead of holding you away from it. You may find this is quite powerful in itself. Menstrual pain is often sharpened (unintentionally) by being kept private, secret, left alone to suffer in silence. Let your breath convey to your pain that she is not alone, that you are there for her. What is that like for her to hear?

If you can, allow your breath, like the lightest touch of a loving hand, to pass across the surface of your pain, softening the holding in your muscles just a little – even 1% can make a significant difference. Once you have managed that first %, the second % is easier. Keep your breath flowing softly and gently so that you can maintain that muscular softening. Gradually let yourself find out how much relaxation you **can** allow, despite the pain…

What does your pain feel like? Let it matter. Let yourself describe it honestly in your journal. Can your pain feel you listening to it? Caring about it? Now begin to listen carefully to how you are emotionally in this bleeding time. Write these feelings down too – they will help you to know what message your pain is wanting to convey to you. Believe the feelings just as they are today – your mind can catch up next week. Stay patient and forgiving, even if you notice that your attention wants to get away from the pain, and stop feeling it. That is very natural. If it happens, check your softening again and see if it needs repeating. Let your breath tell the feelings you have heard them, and you believe them. You don't have to solve them. Just breathe for them, so they can feel accepted.

What if we could simply sit, as our foremothers did long ago – open to the force of our bleeding and willing to let its gravitational pull take us down through our own birth canal into the realms beyond? Down from the head, through the heart, the belly

the world within women

and lower back; down through our interior passageway between the worlds. The nature of menstrual pain makes us want to open up, let down, ease the pressure and congestion we feel. It is a bearing-down pain, an aching need to let go.

In menstruation, when we labour to birth our own Self, when we stand at the doorway between our conscious and unconscious worlds, we need the same single-focus as a woman birthing a baby. Access to menstruation's world is hard-won. It takes fenomenal courage and staying-power. It can make us sweat, pant and groan. It can keep us awake at night. It can stop us, or at least insistently distract us from ordinary rational tasks.

Yet this is the supreme time to access our dreams, intuitions, inner-knowings – our visionary self who is not diluted or distracted by the demands of the rational world. This is the phase of our other-knowing (like reflections in water), our seeing-in-the-dark.

How willing would you be to let your menstruation matter enough that you spend some dedicated time with it each month? To give it a room of its own in the house of your life, so it does not have to knock so loudly on your door at each period?

Special features of menstruation

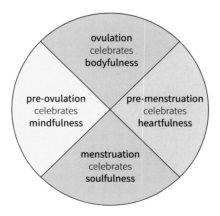

Interiority: including soul and spirituality in our ordinary, daily life

In our foremothers' times the spiritual tasks of menstruation were known and revered, and no other demands were placed on women at this time. Here in the 21st Century, something in us still innately seems to hear their call: our body pulls us downward, but our mind struggles and resists, not knowing how to take the journey, for the culture of mind-science has revoked our passports to travel to these ir-rational destinations. Words such as 'deep', 'low', 'down' and 'dark' have all come to carry negative connotations, to be seen as states to be avoided or fixed, and not at all as places of profound value to be visited regularly and positively in the normal course of a healthy life. The femenome, through menstruation, will do all it can to restore to its rightful place this depth-territory which has been cut off from us by our fear of 'going under'.

In the Laws of Nature things work because *all* parts of a whole are present in balance. The very existence of life is in the coming-together of opposite energies, male and female, to make the *whole*. Listen to the word 'whole' – can you hear how close it is to 'holy'? Life is holy, sacred, perfect, when, and because, *all* of its elements are present. We love summer, but if it continued all year no crops or flocks could renew themselves, and life would quickly die out. Summer can only be its exuberant and fruitful self because winter, the seed phase of life's eternal cycle, stands cool and deep and inward at the opposite pole.

> What is whole is holy, sacred, perfect

Menstruation is the whole-making phase of our cycle. Its completion. To make something whole is to perfect it – make it perfect. The femenome perfects us at menstruation, and again in a much bigger way at cronehood, by ensuring we go inward to find the fourth dimension of our own nature, our fourth faculty of soul or spirituality.

the world within women

a pause to reflect...
Conscious menstruation exercise

During your menstruation (or at the dark of the moon if you are not cycling) give yourself time to be still, quiet and introspective. Allow your awareness to go downward and inward, as your body naturally invites. Open to your thoughts, feelings, insights, longings, intuitions, knowings, dreams, sensations, hunches, glimpses and intimations, whispers, meditational revelations, visions, guidance, wishes, impulses – all that comes to you in the dreamy state and special perspective of this inward time. Write and draw it all in your journal or on your mendala.

Choose one inspiration / realisation / awareness / revelation that feels important to your menstrual self, and **allow yourself to fully believe it.** Even if, or especially if, it is different from your usual, more rational way of seeing things. Get to know it intimately. Write, contemplate and day-dream about how your life would feel if you were living from this perspective. What would it want you to do, believe, think and prioritise differently?

As your cycle moves on, take this soul-instruction with you into your next phases, and be open to learning how you can integrate it consciously into your everyday way of living, mentally, physically and emotionally as you travel around your month – maybe all at once, or maybe little by little. If ways of doing so are not clear to you, ask to be shown what you don't yet know, and stay open and curious, even (especially) if what your menstrual self suggested doesn't easily fit into your 'normal' life.

Pay special attention to your dreams all around the month – they can help us in different ways than our mind is able to. Be relaxed and open to having fun with this. Your soul will love your willingness to let it have a say in its own language in your life!

The art of the pause: menstruation as our monthly sabbatical

The word Sabbath exists in various forms in at least 36 languages, and its sacred connotations of time out to rest, be replenished, and acknowledge the inner, spiritual dimensions of life are part of many different religious traditions. It is thought to originate in Babylonian times, where Sabbatu was a monthly holiday acknowledging the menstruation of the moon goddess Ishtar[34]. The public practice of allowing no work to be done while she was bleeding also appears in the Judeo/Christian commandment to 'keep holy the Sabbath day', although that interpretation has its roots in God resting on the seventh day of his creation of the world. Cherokee Indians marked a monthly rest day at the dark of the moon, which they characterised as 'un-time' or 'non-days', and dedicated to prayer and quiet contemplation.

The theme of sacred necessity in marking times of pause and rest for purification, restoration and spiritual orientation on a weekly, monthly or annual basis has a universal reach in human history. It is seldom acknowledged in our current times, but one form in which it does still exist is the academic tradition of sabbatical leave, where scholars and teachers are given extended periods away from the usual responsibilities of their positions to write, study, fill up or refresh their knowledge and energy. Otherwise, sadly, there is little patience or respect nowadays for this built-in requirement in the design of life, and we try in far too many ways to make our activity, commerce, economics and resource-use continue without the pauses so necessary to maintaining balance and sustainable energy.

It is not easy for us, living in times when pausing is seen as counter-productive, to be able to say yes to our natural monthly Sabbath at menstruation. Many of us live lives of such pace and pressure that the very idea of pausing is a cause for alarm. Sadly, it is this very great contrast between what we need and what we are allowed at this time of the month that causes most of the menstrual ills we suffer. If the demands of your life are such that taking time out at menstruation is unthinkable, know you are not alone – but also do not give up. Do not resign yourself to that old resistance-remedy of carrying on regardless, but instead see if you can be open to micro-steps toward the very big changes that are needed in our societies.

Given that, as we noted above, menstruation completes and makes whole the circle of our cycle, we could call the onset of our period our monthly wholly-day. And as soon as you

---

34   Nor Hall, *The Moon and the Virgin*, The Women's Press, London, 1980. See also Lara Owen, Honoring Menstruation, p 69.

say that word aloud you will hear how the cadence of 'holy-day' becomes 'holiday'. Holidays *are* sacred, because they renew the energy of life. The few businesses who have so far had the wisdom to allow women menstrual leave have not suffered a loss in production, but on the contrary have benefitted considerably from their female staff's refreshed energy on their return from it.

How might you begin, this very month, to contemplate allowing yourself a monthly sabbatical at your period? Notice I said 'contemplate' – a nicely softened-down menstrual approach that will help us not to rush this or make token efforts that don't work and are then abandoned. As with everything in conscious menstruality, this step will not be successful if we only engage with it at a mind level. This is not about the *idea* of menstrual wholly-days, but about the *feeling*, the *bodily sensation* of them that really can, as we have seen, transform our relationship with our hormonal life and womanly wellbeing.

It takes a lot of courage, self-belief, and hopefully the company and support of other women around you, to take the counter-culture steps of living a cycle-logical life. I would suggest that before making any plans at all for time out at your menstruation, you begin to cultivate the art of the pause in general – perhaps as something of an acclimatisation or a calming of resistance that will then become the foundation for further steps.

a pause to reflect...
Cultivating the art of the pause

Feel again the pause at the bottom of your breath cycle (go back to the exercise on p 179 if you would like to be reminded how to get there) – and allow yourself to stay in it for a moment, relaxing deeply. Open to the sensation of completion. Savour it fully. Let your whole nervous system register it. And then the natural turning within you to the promise of a new beginning with your next breath.

Repeat this little step as often as you can during your days. Let it become sweetly enjoyable.

This is especially beneficial to do at the completion of any task, before moving on to the next one. Practice this until you **never** move on to the next thing without a micro-pause to acknowledge what has just been completed. Can you become as conscious and as appreciative of what you **have** done as you are preoccupied with what is in front of you to be done **next**? What happens in your body when you allow the pause?

Do I allow pauses in my life? What makes this difficult? How can I begin to cultivate even micro-pauses regularly in my life: with my breath, my moments of completion, my meal breaks, my evenings and nights, weekends, holidays? How might I bring sacred Sabbaths into the balance of my life? What are the ways, from tiny steps to major ones? When and how do I allow myself to let go in my life? To rest?

Practice cultivating internal spaciousness throughout your month: physically, emotionally, mentally and spiritually. Even steps as simple as a momentary relaxation of muscular or mental holding every time you think of it will help to re-set your energetic system toward allowing painless menstruation.

Once you have developed the art of the pause to the point where you are totally convinced of its pleasures and benefits, you will be in a good place to know that you really are allowed to create menstrual Sabbaths for yourself. You can take it gradually – maybe even starting with a five-minute-total-rest-because-you-are-menstruating, or a relaxing cup of tea in the garden, to see how that feels.

It is *how* you provide this for yourself that matters much more than *what* you provide. How lovingly can you be your own mother, offering yourself gestures of comfort and grace that can most enhance your menstrual time?

What creates the feeling for you of your soul's deep needs being taken care of? Reading

the world within women

a book in the sun for an hour? Having an afternoon nap? A long, slow walk on the beach? Doing nothing at all for a whole afternoon? A deep, scented bath? Music? A special fragrance that you use only at this time of the month? Lying on Mother Earth's heart, in the long grass? Time alone? Time with other women? The possibilities are endless, and there is no right way to do this – only your way.

> It is *how* you give yourself menstrual Sabbaths not *what* you do that makes all the difference… How *lovingly* can you be your own mother at menstruation?

For women who are mothers, it can be helpful to have a group, or at least two of you, dedicated to supporting each other to have menstrual Sabbaths. How might you arrange with other mothers to swap child-care, errands, school transport or cooked meals at each other's menstrual times, so that everyone gets at least one special hour, or morning, or evening, to herself at that time of her month? Remember, the (apparently) smallest steps make the biggest difference, because they invest conscious love and energy into letting your menstrual cycles matter. I have been amazed time and time again at women's reports of how their cycles have changed, sometimes in very major ways, simply from receiving more awareness and attention.

Menstrual Sabbaths will not work if they are a pressure or a 'discipline'. One tiny gesture, made as an act of love, will be of vastly more benefit than anything done because we think we should.

May your menstrual times increasingly become holydays for you, special times of re-creation, refreshment, and delicious dives into the depths of yourself.

x

At a glance...

Inward Energy
Empty
Closed
Dark
Invisible
Contemplative

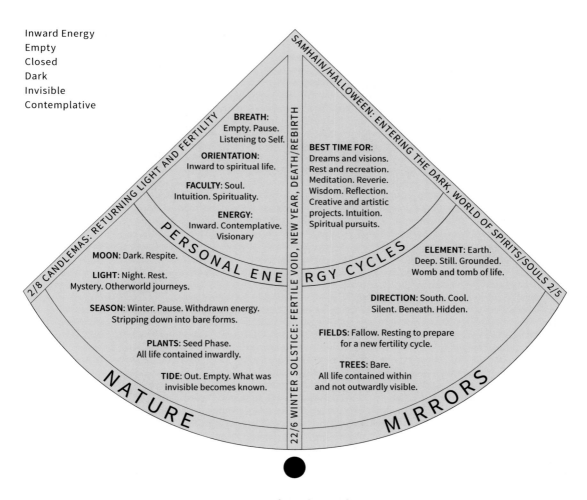

SAMHAIN/HALLOWEEN: ENTERING THE DARK, WORLD OF SPIRITS/SOULS 2/5

2/8 CANDLEMAS: RETURNING LIGHT AND FERTILITY

22/6 WINTER SOLSTICE: FERTILE VOID, NEW YEAR, DEATH/REBIRTH

PERSONAL ENERGY CYCLES

NATURE MIRRORS

BREATH: Empty. Pause. Listening to Self.

ORIENTATION: Inward to spiritual life.

FACULTY: Soul. Intuition. Spirituality.

ENERGY: Inward. Contemplative. Visionary

MOON: Dark. Respite.

LIGHT: Night. Rest. Mystery. Otherworld journeys.

SEASON: Winter. Pause. Withdrawn energy. Stripping down into bare forms.

PLANTS: Seed Phase. All life contained inwardly.

TIDE: Out. Empty. What was invisible becomes known.

BEST TIME FOR: Dreams and visions. Rest and recreation. Meditation. Reverie. Wisdom. Reflection. Creative and artistic projects. Intuition. Spiritual pursuits.

ELEMENT: Earth. Deep. Still. Grounded. Womb and tomb of life.

DIRECTION: South. Cool. Silent. Beneath. Hidden.

FIELDS: Fallow. Resting to prepare for a new fertility cycle.

TREES: Bare. All life contained within and not outwardly visible.

Menstruation Phase Chart

PART FOUR

Re-Storing
our femenome way of life

CHAPTER EIGHT

Mendala magic: letting the femenome run your life!

The path of conscious menstruality is in its essence a path of initiation, with all the dimensions of an epic. There is much to learn along the way, and as with any undertaking that involves acquiring both knowledge *and* the wisdom to use it well, it takes us years to traverse each stage. So, now that we have learned a little about the four foundational building-blocks of our femininity, helpfully separated out for us by the ever-changing seasons of our menstrual cycle, it is time for us to consider how they all fit together in the big picture of the femenome. As you can imagine, a map of the whole design would be well beyond the scope of this book – and in fact impossible to draw. It would be like trying to chart every star in the firmament, as one realisation leads to another, and another. So this chapter will give you just a few introductory suggestions as to how you might begin to live in a more cycle-logical way, and receive some of the benefits of allowing the fenomena of the femenome to have their way with you.

The most important thing for you in reading this book is to understand it not as an instruction manual for you to follow, but as an invitation for you to embark on your own quest; to discover, month by month, the unique and infinitely detailed revelations of your own personal femenome. There will be no other quite like yours. The examples I am giving are broad and generic so that there is plenty of room within them for your own experiences.

As you know, the mendala is a specialised form of mandala. A mandala, in its original Sanskrit language, is a container of sacred space, a way of representing the universe in a small circle. Mandalas have been used as expressions of the sacred and the infinite right across cultures and time. Our femenome mendala is a very special form of mandala in that it is not static, but alive, dynamic, constantly flowing and changing, expanding and deepening. A mendala is like a mirror. It will hold and reflect back to us *every* part of who we are. It does not pick and choose, reveal some parts and hide others. It does not judge, condemn or favour. It does not portray 'good' sides and 'bad' sides, as our mind likes to do. A mendala simply says *this is who you are. This is what you are made of.* It is a supreme teacher for us of the very necessary arts of acceptance and compassion for *all* parts of ourself.

Because our menstruality is the carrier of life, it must contain **all** the ingredients needed to make a person whole – so that it can transmit them not only to us, but to the children we create through its life-giving functions.

created by life to create life

This makes our menstrual cycle a perfect template of wholeness and balance. Every aspect in a mandala, and therefore in a mendala, holds its mirror image directly opposite. Because of its constant, centrifugal spin (like the spin phase in our washing machine cycle) the femenome's developmental impulses move outward from our centre like ripples on a pond, ensuring an all-encompassing, all-expanding pattern of growth that leaves nothing untouched inside us. The beauty of this is that whatever we encounter and successfully respond to at *any* point of our cycle is quite literally 'circulated' to *every* part of us. An accomplishment I 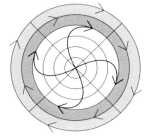 achieve at ovulation – say a new step in confidence – spins out to become available in my whole energy system: to be felt emotionally at pre-menstruation, integrated into my sense of self at menstruation, and given further new ways of expressing itself in action at pre-ovulation. In this way our outer, experience-in-the-world life and our deep inner-consciousness life are constantly co-creating, nourishing and expanding each other in a rich and mutually enhancing two-way flow.

the world within women

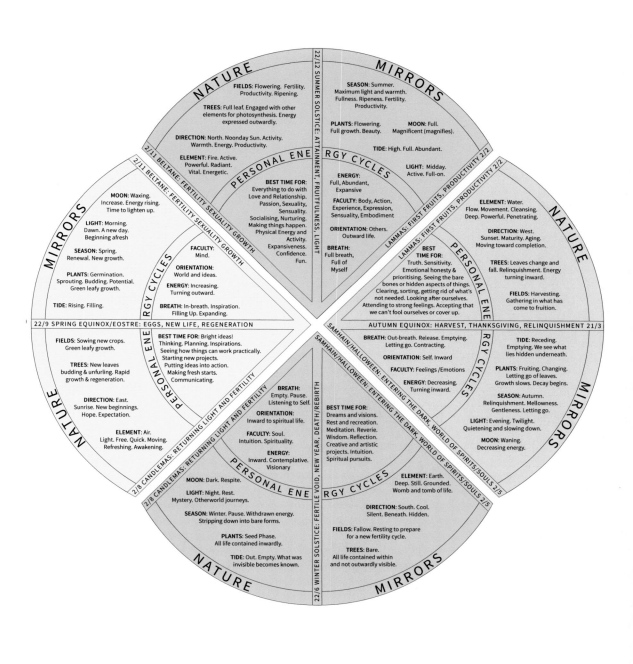

SUMMER SOLSTICE: ATTAINMENT, FRUITFULNESS, LIGHT 22/12

NATURE

MIRRORS

FIELDS: Flowering. Fertility. Productivity. Ripening.

TREES: Full leaf. Engaged with other elements for photosynthesis. Energy expressed outwardly.

DIRECTION: North. Noonday Sun. Activity. Warmth. Energy. Productivity.

ELEMENT: Fire. Active. Powerful. Radiant. Vital. Energetic.

SEASON: Summer. Maximum light and warmth. Fullness. Ripeness. Fertility. Productivity.

PLANTS: Flowering. Full growth. Beauty.

MOON: Full. Magnificent (magnifies).

TIDE: High. Full. Abundant.

LIGHT: Midday. Active. Full-on.

PERSONAL ENERGY CYCLES

BEST TIME FOR: Everything to do with Love and Relationship. Passion, Sexuality, Sensuality. Socialising, Nurturing. Making things happen. Physical Energy and Activity. Expansiveness. Confidence. Fun.

ENERGY: Full, Abundant, Expansive

FACULTY: Body, Action, Experience, Expression, Sensuality, Embodiment

ORIENTATION: Others. Outward life.

BREATH: Full breath, Full of Myself

2/11 BELTANE: FERTILITY SEXUALITY GROWTH

MIRRORS

MOON: Waxing. Increase. Energy rising. Time to lighten up.

LIGHT: Morning. Dawn. A new day. Beginning afresh

SEASON: Spring. Renewal. New growth.

PLANTS: Germination. Sprouting. Budding. Potential. Green leafy growth.

TIDE: Rising. Filling.

FACULTY: Mind.

ORIENTATION: World and ideas.

ENERGY: Increasing. Turning outward.

BREATH: In-breath. Inspiration. Filling Up. Expanding.

PERSONAL ENERGY CYCLES

LAMMAS: FIRST FRUITS, PRODUCTIVITY 2/2

NATURE

ELEMENT: Water. Flow. Movement. Cleansing. Deep. Powerful. Penetrating.

DIRECTION: West. Sunset. Maturity. Aging. Moving toward completion.

TREES: Leaves change and fall. Relinquishment. Energy turning inward.

FIELDS: Harvesting. Gathering in what has come to fruition.

PERSONAL ENERGY CYCLES

BEST TIME FOR: Truth. Sensitivity. Emotional honesty & prioritising. Seeing the bare bones or hidden aspects of things. Clearing, sorting, getting rid of what's not needed. Looking after ourselves. Attending to strong feelings. Accepting that we can't fool ourselves or cover up.

BEST TIME FOR: Bright ideas! Thinking. Planning. Inspirations. Seeing how things can work practically. Starting new projects. Putting ideas into action. Making fresh starts. Communicating.

22/9 SPRING EQUINOX/EOSTRE: EGGS, NEW LIFE, REGENERATION

FIELDS: Sowing new crops. Green leafy growth.

TREES: New leaves budding & unfurling. Rapid growth & regeneration.

DIRECTION: East. Sunrise. New beginnings. Hope. Expectation.

ELEMENT: Air. Light. Free. Quick. Moving. Refreshing. Awakening.

NATURE

AUTUMN EQUINOX: HARVEST, THANKSGIVING, RELINQUISHMENT 21/3

BREATH: Out-breath. Release. Emptying. Letting go. Contracting.

ORIENTATION: Self. Inward

FACULTY: Feelings /Emotions

ENERGY: Decreasing. Turning inward.

TIDE: Receding. Emptying. We see what lies hidden underneath.

PLANTS: Fruiting. Changing. Letting go of leaves. Growth slows. Decay begins.

SEASON: Autumn. Relinquishment. Mellowness. Gentleness. Letting go.

LIGHT: Evening. Twilight. Quietening and slowing down.

MOON: Waning. Decreasing energy.

MIRRORS

SAMHAIN/HALLOWEEN: ENTERING THE DARK, WORLD OF SPIRITS/SOULS 2/5

BEST TIME FOR: Dreams and visions. Rest and recreation. Meditation. Reverie. Wisdom. Reflection. Creative and artistic projects. Intuition. Spiritual pursuits.

BREATH: Empty. Pause. Listening to Self.

ORIENTATION: Inward to spiritual life.

FACULTY: Soul. Intuition. Spirituality.

ENERGY: Inward. Contemplative. Visionary

2/8 CANDLEMAS: RETURNING LIGHT AND FERTILITY

PERSONAL ENERGY CYCLES

MOON: Dark. Respite.

LIGHT: Night. Rest. Mystery. Otherworld journeys.

SEASON: Winter. Pause. Withdrawn energy. Stripping down into bare forms.

PLANTS: Seed Phase. All life contained inwardly.

TIDE: Out. Empty. What invisible becomes known.

NATURE

22/6 WINTER SOLSTICE: FERTILE VOID, NEW YEAR, DEATH/REBIRTH

ELEMENT: Earth. Deep. Still. Grounded. Womb and tomb of life.

DIRECTION: South. Cool. Silent. Beneath. Hidden.

FIELDS: Fallow. Resting to prepare for a new fertility cycle.

TREES: Bare. All life contained within and not outwardly visible.

MIRRORS

Like any alive thing, the mendala can be drawn in an endless variety of ways, always expressing the fourfold impulse of life itself, and the constant movement of evolution within the stability of a perfectly balanced structure. Here is another form you might enjoy, showing the way in which menstruality energies are constantly moving outward from, and back inward through, our centre, flowing us on from one phase to the next. In this mendala we can also easily see how it is made up of two crossed infinity symbols for the four spiritual directions: upward and downward, inward and outward, and showing how the ever-expanding four-directional flow of the femenome will take us as far as we are willing to go in each of them.

Or you can make yourself a mendala that is a four-petalled flower, and use it to get on intimate terms with each of your petals – their colours, shapes, fragrances – and the perfect and gorgeous blossom they make as a whole.

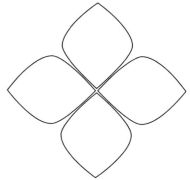

Women in my Luna House courses have devised all sorts of wonderful ways to make themselves whole mendalas. Some have put together the *At-a-glance* charts of each phase to create the whole picture of their month. One enthusiast announced that she was going to make a huge mendala to put on her kitchen wall, with a clock hand indicating her progression around her cycle so that her whole family could see it and come to know its rhythms. What a wonderful thing this would be in our workplaces too! And – as our growing consciousness of the femenome causes the world's women to synchronise with the moon once again – in our town plazas, city halls, parks, and thoroughfares. Imagine that – a mendala clock right beside every time-clock in the world's public places!

Do play around with mendalas. They can be the most wonderful tool for inspiration, creativity, insights and fun. You can make them for anything: what music resonates with you at your different cycle phases? What foods appeal most? What kind of places in Nature feel right to be in as your inner world changes?

Here's my places-to-be mendala: what is yours?

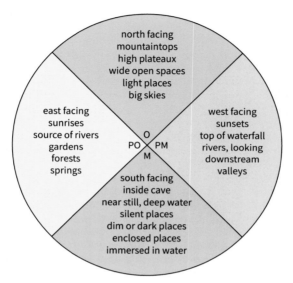

Menstruality – attuned places to be

The creative possibilities are endless. Have fun with your mendala-makings. Let them be playthings, works of art, colour, dance, music, yoga, sound, form: any and every means of creative expression for any and every facet of life.

Whatever form you like to use, draw and colour it in ways that help you feel its flow and flavours circulating inside you, just like your blood, your breath – and just like the currents and winds that are the blood and breath of Planet Earth. Feel your mendala's patterns gathering up *every* aspect of you – those you are already at ease with and those more wild or tender that are not so well known to you. Feel what it is like to dare to include them all: the secret and the sensitive, the frail and the feisty, the mundane and the magical – letting no part feel itself too modest or too magnificent to be included.

> **Conscious menstruality is designed to bring us**
> wholeness of Self
> + balance and inclusion of ALL aspects
> + complete self-knowledge
> + courageous self-acceptance
> + development into our fullest potential
> = **THE GIFT OF SELF-POSSESSION**

We women quite literally *have it in us* – we have what it takes coursing through our bodies – to heal the imbalance, the fears, hatreds and exclusions that are devastating our world. Our fenomenal wisdom – the month by month learning of *exactly what it takes* to reconcile our own internal differences – qualifies us uniquely to teach our societies to heal themselves by including all the various peoples, beliefs and cultures of this world without judgement or prejudice. Just imagine what it might be like if our woman politicians were allowed to be truly female: if they were charged with working through their mendalas to shine the light of each of their cycle viewpoints on policies and priorities; if the true qualities of mothering were to guide our senates and parliaments; if deeply felt emotions and spiritual discernments were given their place of influence in how our world is run. It is not too much to ask! This is what we *can have*, as women all over the globe remember and reclaim what we have to offer.

> What will the world be like:
>
> When women politicians are charged with working through their mendalas to create life-honouring policies incorporating each cycle perspective?
>
> When the priorities of mothering guide our senates and parliaments?
>
> When clear and conscious emotional and spiritual values shape the way humanity charts its course?

Dimensions within dimensions:
weaving our inner and outer life together

Within the hum of our cycle's centrifugal spin around the axis of our Self, some interesting overtones and undertones can be heard if we wish to listen, perhaps similar to the multi-toned sound of a Tibetan singing bowl. As we become more and more familiar with the song of our cycle it will reveal dimensions that can widen and deepen without limit, lending a deliciously feminine intrigue to the ancient axiom:

~ The whole is greater than the sum of its parts ~

We will explore these in much greater depth in later books in the femenome series. But for now, as a simple example, let's look at just one layer in a little more detail. As we have already observed, there is a second movement within our cycle's fourfold circuit, an oscillation, or rocking motion that is much like the rising and falling ocean tides caused by Earth's daily revolutions. This is the femenome's constant strobing of our life through the dark and the light phases of the moon, matching the inner and outer developmental pivots of our lives. There is profound purpose in this, and endless potential for our personal expansion. As with everything in conscious menstruality, a good place to begin is by simply observing, and journaling or mendala-making to become acquainted with our own personal movements and inter-weavings between our inner world of consciousness and our outer world of experience across every area of our life: personal, relational, work, social, recreational, operational, dream-life, etc.

For example, you may observe whether there are times in your month when you are fascinated with what's going on in the world, glued to the news, eager to get involved and be a mover and shaker in your community. And then other times when it all feels too much, and you find yourself sobbing through every bulletin because it's unbearably touching or tragic. Now you just want to leave all that to other people, and wrap yourself up in a quiet and solitary place to meditate.

Do you sometimes revel in being the wonder-woman mother who can do a million things at once, and then the very next week find yourself wishing your husband and children would all just go away and stop wanting you?

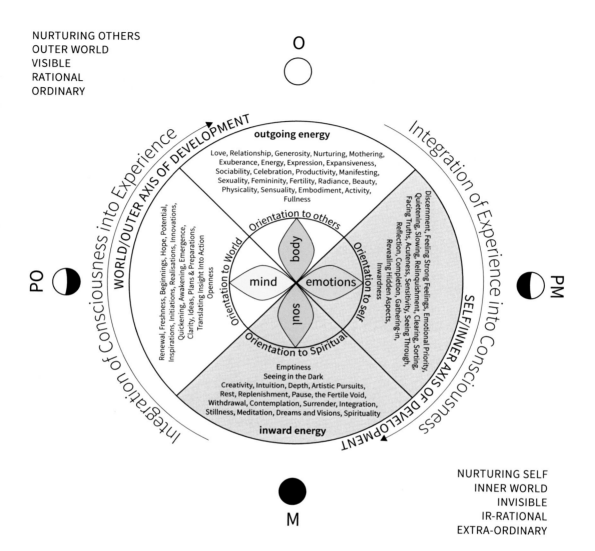

NURTURING OTHERS
OUTER WORLD
VISIBLE
RATIONAL
ORDINARY

O

outgoing energy

Love, Relationship, Generosity, Nurturing, Mothering,
Exuberance, Energy, Expression, Expansiveness,
Sociability, Celebration, Productivity, Manifesting,
Sexuality, Femininity, Fertility, Radiance, Beauty,
Physicality, Sensuality, Embodiment, Activity,
Fullness

Orientation to others

Orientation to World

body
mind emotions
soul

Orientation to self

Orientation to Spiritual

Discernment, Feeling Strong Feelings, Emotional Priority,
Quietening, Slowing, Relinquishment, Clearing, Sorting,
Facing Truths, Acuteness, Sensitivity, Seeing Through,
Reflection, Completion, Gathering-in,
Revealing Hidden Aspects,
Inwardness

Renewal, Freshness, Beginnings, Hope, Potential,
Inspirations, Initiations, Realisations, Innovations,
Quickening, Awakening, Emergence,
Clarity, Ideas, Plans & Preparations,
Translating Insight Into Action
Openness

Emptiness
Seeing in the Dark
Creativity, Intuition, Depth, Artistic Pursuits,
Rest, Replenishment, Pause, the Fertile Void,
Withdrawal, Contemplation, Surrender, Integration,
Stillness, Meditation, Dreams and Visions, Spirituality

inward energy

WORLD/OUTER AXIS OF DEVELOPMENT

Integration of Consciousness into Experience

Integration of Experience into Consciousness

SELF/INNER AXIS OF DEVELOPMENT

PO

PM

M

NURTURING SELF
INNER WORLD
INVISIBLE
IR-RATIONAL
EXTRA-ORDINARY

Each phase complements, supports and enhances all others.
Our menstrual cycle is the quintessential template
of developmental balance and wholeness

the femenomal energy flows of the whole menstrual cycle

What if we can come to a place where the apparently contradictory parts of our nature
begin to make so much sense to us that they become mutually enhancing, rather than
vexingly disruptive of each other?

the world within women

Here is a simple chart of generalised menstruality fenomena which can serve as an example for you to work from as you map out your own movement between your inner and outer worlds around your cycle. *Your* mendala will note feelings and activities that are specific and current in *your* actual life circumstances, so that you can really see what light *your* changing cycle fenomena can bring to things *you* are dealing with on a day by day basis.

It's important to know our natural compass bearings, and how they swing and vary around our month, because they *all* have something equally valuable to contribute to the things we care about in the world. Women who are politically passionate and engaged will need their times of inward nourishment to ensure that vital energy is replenished and sustainable, and also to enhance their activism with the wisdom that comes from our deep spiritual reference points. And a mother who gets regular me-time to refresh her wellsprings is much more likely to succeed in being the bottomless well of love and patience she wishes to be for her children.

Our cycle is wondrously designed to ensure we don't get stuck in tunnel vision about anything. Knowing the rise and fall, ebb and flow, ins and outs of our feminine energies helps us not to fixate on one way of being, believing it to be our 'right' or (goddess forbid) 'normal' state, but to have confidence in how each can contribute to an easy flow in our life. Just like the enhanced sensory experiences we can get at the movies these days, the femenome compels us to experience our lives in surround-sound and 4D viewing. Although we have been taught to resist and distrust our multi-channel way of life, we really have every right to feel immensely proud of our highly refined ability to live in such a sophisticated way.

> A simple mendala can help us figure something out or get a fuller picture of it. Mendalas are a marvellous tool for self-therapy.

Sometimes even a simple mendala can help us figure something out or get a more comprehensive picture of it. They can be an excellent tool for self-therapy, as I had to learn myself in the very intense years of trying to develop this work through all the ups and downs, ins and outs of my own cycle. I had only my cycle to teach me my cycle, and much of the time I learned the hard way. For me the recurring feelings at pre-menstruation were despair, grief and a strangling conviction of failure at my inability to progress my mission as quickly as I wanted to. Only slowly, and very, very painfully, did I learn to allow these near-fatal feelings to show me the depth of my hope, my desire, my willingness to bring the knowledge of the femenome to women throughout the world – even though I did not know how to, and could not see my way ahead. Gradually I realised that my pre-menstrual despair was the mirror-image of my pre-ovulational hope – the same feeling experienced in opposite ways – and an immense reassurance of how very much I wanted to fulfil my soul's purpose in this life.

It took me a long time – and I hope it will not take you as long nor cost you as much – to realise that what appeared to be a wild and random swing in my cycle from hope to despair and back again each month was actually something much more graceful. In my avid determination to get this knowledge into a form where women could have it and use it, I put tremendous mental pressure on myself to forge ahead with my project, totally destroying the life-balance that would have sustained me had I known it then. All along, what the wise femenome was trying to teach me was that to succeed in my mission I had to *use all four phases of my cycle,* not just the out-there-doing-it side of my moon. My mind was all geared up to achieve the **outer work** – to make conscious menstruality happen in the world – but my cycle kept hauling me back to do the **inner work,** the hard yards of knowing and healing my own shadows and accepting my own needs, which of course I had swept aside in my absolute willingness to serve my outer purpose.

Needless to say, and even though I had to be dragged kicking and screaming all the way, once I let the femenome herself guide me I discovered that the knowledge I was seeking to bring to you was not to be found in all that mental striving, all that trying harder. If you look back again at the diagram on p 210 you will see around the rim of the mendala one of the most beautiful and illuminating fenomena of the whole menstrual cycle – the constant rocking or hula-hooping movement created by its flow between our inner and outer life.

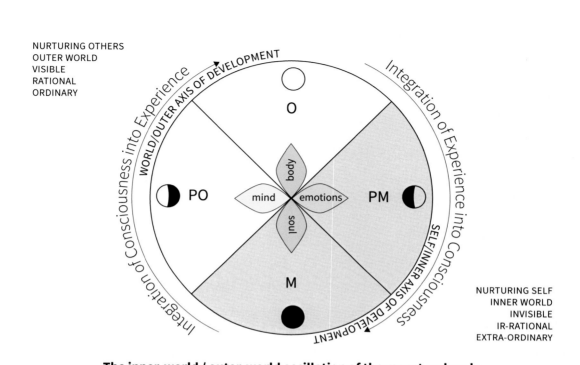

The inner-world / outer-world oscillation of the menstrual cycle

We can almost feel the *two* hands of the femenome on us – shaping our two sides, inner life and outer life, alternately and symmetrically – as we spin between them on her potter's wheel. In this deft and delicate balance, our external, active life in the busy world is constantly informed and enriched by the *consciousness* we've brought with us from our inner world in the preceding two cycle weeks: soul expressed in action. And then we cross back again into pre-menstruation's contemplative state, bringing all we have learned and absorbed from our *experience* to create further layers of inner consciousness: action integrated into soul.

> In the constant cross-fertilising of our cycle, our active life in the outer world is informed and enriched by the **consciousness** we've brought from our inner world; while our inner world is fed in turn by the **experience** we've gained from our activity.

Despite its natural and compelling logic, I confess this balancing art of dedication to my own inner life was a lesson I was not initially willing to accept, as (and I suspect many of you will resonate with this) it felt like a luxury I could not afford – something I loved, but could not spare the time for. Alas, my wilful efforts to try harder and yet harder persisted for many years, until I finally did learn that a single hour of daydreaming – or simply lying in bed a few extra moments before leaping out to work at my desk – could contribute far more to the success of my work than a hundred exhausted hours at the keyboard. That the parts of my cycle in which I thought I was not succeeding were actually a goldmine of knowledge so fine and deep it needed stillness to become visible. It was not until I learned to *trust* that my ir-rational faculties really could add to my work (and in fact show me an unending flow of wondrous things I did not know I knew) that I could relax and value my inner world. And at this point, of course, my pre-menstrual despairs ceased to torment me, knowing I had at last heard their message.

Being unafraid of the strong feelings of pre-menstruation can help us get out of a repetitive pattern we may be stuck in with our cycle. My stuck pattern (are any of its elements familiar to you?) was:

And then, as I went on in my own apprenticeship in conscious menstruality, I discovered the most exciting thing – that the femenome could teach me to create a widening, outward-spiralling scope of possibilities around my cycle:

the world within women

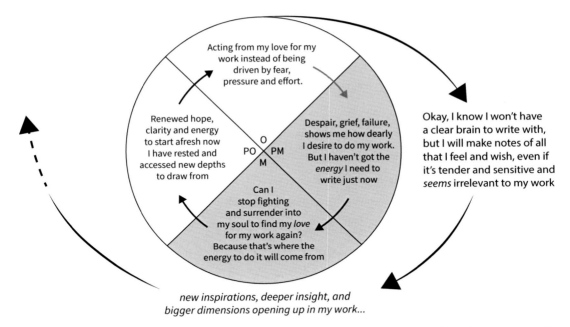

Acting from my love for my work instead of being driven by fear, pressure and effort.

Renewed hope, clarity and energy to start afresh now I have rested and accessed new depths to draw from

Despair, grief, failure, shows me how dearly I desire to do my work. But I haven't got the *energy* I need to write just now

O
PO PM
M

Can I stop fighting and surrender into my soul to find my *love* for my work again? Because that's where the energy to do it will come from

Okay, I know I won't have a clear brain to write with, but I will make notes of all that I feel and wish, even if it's tender and sensitive and *seems* irrelevant to my work

new inspirations, deeper insight, and bigger dimensions opening up in my work…

with the potential to endlessly ease and enrich my life and work, and leading eventually to this book and my Luna House teachings.

Do not be discouraged if your learning under the femenome takes quite some time to bring you the results you are seeking. Remember, her answers will always be multi-faceted, multi-layered, and surprisingly different from any that your mind will be looking for, so they can take considerable perseverance (over many months or even years) to fully discern. The beauty of this is that by the time these pearls and diamonds of wisdom emerge into our mind's frame of reference we will see that they have been building inside us, in the rich strata of our other faculties, over time, and have a much more honed and high-fidelity offering to make us because of that. In the times to come, as we reclaim and re-develop our menstruality knowledge, we will need menstruality therapists who have themselves been initiated and apprenticed in the college of the femenome, and who are wise to her ways. In the meantime, working with groups of women who really are willing to open to the feminine in this way will be necessary and supportive.

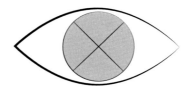

We can look in our personal mendala mirror much as an iridologist looks deeply into our eyes – where are the dark patches that show the troubled or unknown parts of ourself? Are there lines indicating that attention and adjustment are needed? What are these beautiful, intricate patterns we have never noticed before, because we have not looked closely enough? Where are our healthiest and most robust energies? What else is there to see, now that we are searching?

How can the parts that are clear and strong assist those that are struggling? What advice, what remedies, what practical support can they offer? For example, what could my optimistic and clear-thinking pre-ovulational self prepare in advance to support my pre-menstrual self, who can sometimes lose sight of the big picture and slip into despair? Or, how can my wise, calm menstrual self ground and anchor my tendency to be rash or impulsive when I'm ovulating?

Once you have become accustomed to making mendalas for yourself, you can consult them in all sorts of ways to clarify, deepen, support or enhance any aspect of your life. They can of course also be of priceless assistance in any therapeutic process you may be undertaking, if (and only if) your health professional knows how to read them. We can only hope it will become compulsory for every health practitioner who works with women to complete a comprehensive education in the femenome and its languages in the foreseeable future, for mendalas can reveal crucially important information that may not be visible to other forms of investigation.

the world within women

Peta[35] came to me in desperation, having sought assistance from every kind of hormonally-oriented specialist she could find for her debilitating and life-threatening pre-menstrual crises. Each month she would contemplate ending her life, as her deep longings to follow the path she felt to be her soul's purpose seemed to constantly be snatched further and further from her grasp by the return of savage depression, and a loss of energy that would render her unable to leave her bed for days at a time. It is entirely understandable that Peta felt her femaleness was to blame for this constant and severe disruption of her life, and had come to believe that the only remedy would be to chemically or surgically eliminate what seemed to be the source of such great suffering for her.

However, a menstruality iridology approach revealed a very different picture, both of Peta's predicament and of what would be required to resolve it. As our therapy progressed, she slowly began to reveal the profound traumas of her early life in a war-torn country, and the absolute lack of any acknowledgement of, or support for, these since she had re-established herself as a young adult in an unfamiliar country. Naturally, all her effort had gone into leaving her past behind, and seeking to see ahead to where she dearly wished her future life could go. Peta's lifelong dream had been to engage in a field of work that requires a very clear intuitive faculty and acute sensitivity.

Far from obstructing her, as they appeared to be doing, Peta's menstruality disturbances were actually bringing a vital and saving grace to her life and hopes. Careful menstruality iridology revealed that the diagnosis of her disabling predicament was that Peta was trying to go forward without going inward. This could never have worked for her, as the high degree of intuitive ability required for her chosen career would have been clouded by the chaos of unresolved traumas inside her – which were of course making their presence felt each time her pre-menstrual hormones tried to take her into her inner world of emotional truth. Far from being her enemy, Peta's extreme pre-menstrual suffering was quite literally stopping her in her tracks – making it totally impossible for her to go any further forward without going inward and downward. Her PMS was imploring her to find the remedy and relief she deserved and needed for all the pain stored inside her, to free her for the unencumbered future that truly was her destiny.

---

35   All names and details of case-studies in this book have been changed to protect privacy

Sometimes our menstruality hormones really will ask us to seek out help and support to resolve things that are too complex or deep to achieve alone. However, there is a lot we can also do beautifully for ourselves and each other in a femenome-conscious life.

Here is a generalised exercise that you can adapt and use for life-planning, trouble-shooting, deepening self-awareness, self-care, or specific applications. This can be enjoyable, supportive and instructive – fun to do just for yourself, with friends or in groups. Or you can adapt it to a simpler form and use it to help your daughter to get the feel of how to take care of herself in her cycle in those early years.

A pause to reflect...
Becoming your own menstruality iridologist

Map out the energies you know rise and fall in you as you move around your cycle. Stay open and non-judgemental. Note which phases are best suited to which activities, and how you might consciously use the changing energies to best advantage to get things done on **all** levels of your life: practical, emotional, vocational, relational, recreational, spiritual and everything else. When will you do that academic assignment? Which weekend would be best for a meditation retreat? What about that long put-off conversation with your partner? Or the promised trip to the swimming pool with the kids?

Attend to **wholeness** and **balance** in your iridology. And don't forget **enjoyment.** How can you create as much **ease** for yourself as possible? How would it be for your tired and tender pre-menstrual self to find that last week's invincible ovulational woman had made some extra meals and put them in the freezer for these more difficult days? Be a thorough iridologist. Include as much detail as you can.

Look to the Nature-mirrors and personal energy cycles on your menstruality phase charts (pp 111, 128, 169, 199) for support – how can these deepen our understanding, refine our diagnosis, and suggest wise remedies? (For example, how can autumn teach me more about gracefully letting go? What would the full moon suggest about fun ways of expressing all this sexual energy even when I'm single?)

Become a **practising menstruality iridologist**. Stay available to yourself to provide follow-ups as you change and grow through your cycles.

Mendalas for our work life

Here's an example of how this can work. Sally has been observing for some time now how her various strengths and abilities come to the fore at different points around her month, and she has made herself a mendala as a ready reference for her menstruality iridology. Her 'natural aptitude mendala', built up over a couple of years of observations, looks like this:

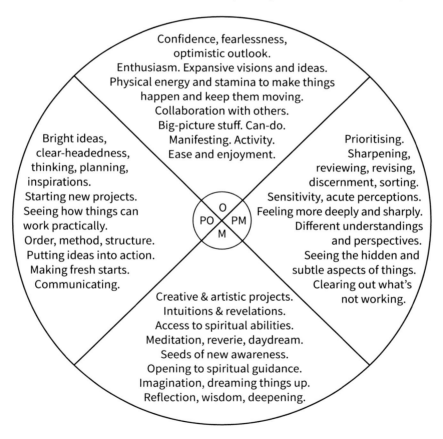

However, when Sally decided to take on some part-time study in addition to her busy work life, things got more complicated, and some new patterns of anxiety and stress began to show up when she had assignments to do. All through the first semester of her course, Sally noticed that she would become tearful, self-doubting, angry and exhausted over her assignments whenever she was pre-menstrual, and that try as she might, nothing worth keeping would get written during those weeks. When her periods came along she would just stop trying. Nothing would stick in her mind, and anything she did write at that time was only more fodder for the delete button. At first this had frightened and horrified her – Sally knew she was a good writer, and had been a straight A student all through her school life. So why was it such hard work now?

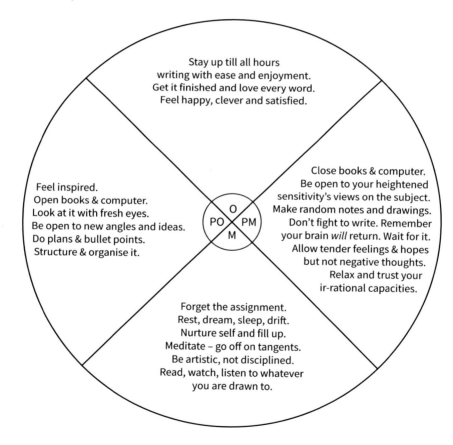

the world within women

At the start of the second semester Sally decided to make herself a special assignment mendala to optimise her chances of getting them written with a minimum of stress and much more enjoyment and ease. It took her several months of somewhat cautious experimenting, to see whether she really could trust that her menstruality would get the job done, despite seeming incapable of it for two weeks of each month. But as she gained confidence and fenomenal courage, Sally eventually came up with an assignment mendala that worked perfectly for her, bringing her good results every time. She keeps adjusting it as she learns more, but her current version of fenomenal wisdom looks something like the diagram opposite.

~◇~

Menstruality energies are designed for the living of life – ours to use to our own advantage in as many ways as we possibly can.

Mendalas for relationship dynamics

Women in relationships might find great benefit in making mendalas for dealing with issues that come up repeatedly, or seem difficult to resolve, no matter how hard we try. A relationship mendala can help us firstly to identify such issues, and see them in sharper focus, and secondly to ensure we are using **all** our capacities in approaching them, and not getting into a stuck cycle. For many of us, the repeating and self-esteem-bruising pattern can run something like this, and sadly relationships often suffer, or even end as the seemingly inescapable pattern of recurrence destroys hope and confidence that things will ever become different. It is

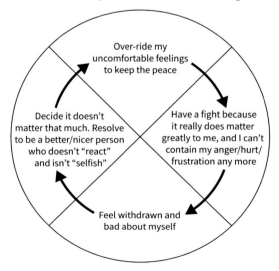

Over-ride my uncomfortable feelings to keep the peace

Have a fight because it really does matter greatly to me, and I can't contain my anger/hurt/frustration any more

Feel withdrawn and bad about myself

Decide it doesn't matter that much. Resolve to be a better/nicer person who doesn't "react" and isn't "selfish"

stuck relationship cycle

all too easy at such times for both women and men to believe that it is our hormones and their cyclical eruptions that put strain on the relationship, and to forget that, used consciously, *the very thing that seems to be creating the disturbance is actually indicating the way to resolution.*

For Helena this pattern showed up in the form of resentful feelings around money that would boil up periodically to ruffle the surface of what was otherwise a very happy and trusting second marriage. These upsetting and unwanted outbursts of anger also disturbed Helena's sense of herself as a loving, contented, generous and even-tempered wife. She felt dismayed, surprised and puzzled that money issues would suddenly seem so oddly important, and cause her to see her husband in a darkened light, when for most of the month they were of no concern to her whatsoever.

A very helpful first step if we recognise this repeating circle around any issue in our relationships (with anyone, but especially our intimate partners) is to make the most honest mendala we can – for ourself only, initially – revealing our true feelings in relation to the issue *all* around the month. Helena undertook this commitment somewhat reluctantly, for reasons that any woman would easily recognise! The intensity of hormonally-heightened feelings can seem very scary to approach, and absolutely not a place where we would expect to find any wisdom or insight that we could trust. It really does take patience and practice of all our conscious menstruality skills to trust that such fiery feelings actually do have something valid and important to say, though their true message is rarely visible at first glance.

As Helena became able to support herself with the "first aid for feelings" practices outlined on p 151–153, and could take the risk of giving voice to her supposedly out-of-order feelings about money, she found to her great surprise and relief that a much more important and relatable dynamic was at play. She needed to see that she was not just an uptight person who was obsessed with money – that her big feelings at pre-menstruation were actually about deeper issues around how she and her husband had agreed, since theirs was a later-in-life marriage, on an arrangement of separate finances *that actually did not feel right for her.* The depth of her emotion, once she was prepared to listen with enough respect to hear its real priorities, showed her that what her deep feminine Self very dearly wanted was the inclusion of true mutuality and deeper commitment with the man she loved. Once she could allow herself to accept how much this meant to her, she was able to take the femenome-enhanced (femenhanced) step of bringing a heartfelt invitation to her husband, that they deepen their relationship into a new way of sharing the resources of their household.

Helena's discovery was an important one. Once we really know how greatly an issue matters, how valid it is, and why it keeps coming up month after month (very likely highlighted when we are pre-menstrual) we will be much better prepared to move ourself and the other on to an unstuck cycle pattern, that can expand a little more each month as we continue to let all of our feminine faculties shine their light on it.

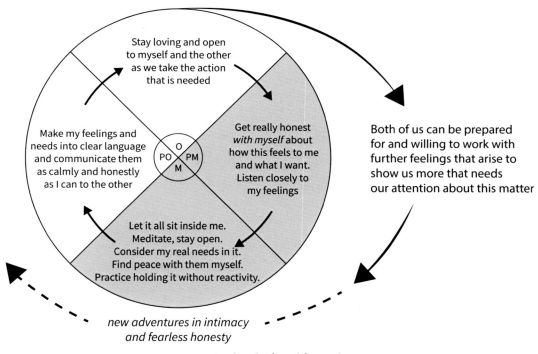

Stay loving and open to myself and the other as we take the action that is needed

Get really honest *with myself* about how this feels to me and what I want. Listen closely to my feelings

Both of us can be prepared for and willing to work with further feelings that arise to show us more that needs our attention about this matter

Make my feelings and needs into clear language and communicate them as calmly and honestly as I can to the other

Let it all sit inside me. Meditate, stay open. Consider my real needs in it. Find peace with them myself. Practice holding it without reactivity.

new adventures in intimacy and fearless honesty

unstuck relationship cycle

The inbuilt thrust of our femenome energies toward ever-increasing consciousness is of course meant not only for our own progression and development, but to refine our relationships into higher states of awareness and potency as well. Where there are conscious or unconscious blocks and limitations in the dynamic that are inhibiting our growth, we can be sure that our super-sensitive menstruality will home in on them and do all it can to ensure that our attempts to over-ride or 'put up with' things that are not in our best interests (and also not in the relationship's best interests) do not succeed. Our ever-alert hormones will to oblige us to feel acutely what we are tempted to deny, giving us the chance to free ourselves and our partners from traps and resistances that make us and our relationships stunted. Perhaps we could call this way of allowing the femenome to hone us in her inexorable ways "femenhoning"!

Recovery mendalas: making our own menstruality iridology prescription

As we become increasingly familiar with our conscious menstruality practices over the years we will grow more and more adept at applying the energies of our cycle to specifically support any need or issue that may arise in our lives. Different aspects of the fenomenal energies will become appropriate and helpful at different times, and in different circumstances. You may like to experiment with designing your own recovery mendala flower, or whole bouquets of them, as experiences and challenges present themselves from time to time on your path. Choose from the teachings of each cycle phase and collect up whichever four mendala petals will suit your situation and offer you the best support at any given time.

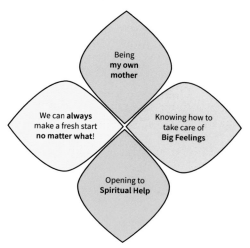

This is a recovery mendala flower that helped me greatly at a time when I was in such despair that I just did not know how to go on in my life. If I could just manage to find the little glimmer of hope I remembered to look for each month in the pre-ovulation petal; the non-judgemental motherly love and acceptance that the ovulation petal offered; the response-ability I knew my anguish needed at pre-menstruation, and the great consolation of realising I was not alone spiritually as menstruation took me into its surrendering petal, I could (and did) make it alive through a long winter of struggle and soul-deep grief.

Because they are soul-designed specifically to assist our growth and enhance our lives the femenome's lessons will *always* be available to us – like our very own inbuilt therapist, spiritual teacher, physician, and en-cyclo-paedia of personalised remedies, open for consultations 24/7/52. It's nice to put your recovery mendala flower on your wall, or somewhere where you can see it effortlessly and follow it around the months until it has served its purpose so well that it's time to make a new one.

Once we become experienced and confident in creating and using these for ourselves (and that means being very realistic about the amount of patience and perseverance that might be needed to get the results we want) we can also make recovery mendala flowers for our friends, colleagues or daughters.

Or mendala flowers can serve as lovely any-occasion greeting cards, simply by making a menstruality-acknowledging wish, prayer or offering for each phase of another woman's month…

Kairos time: a cycle-logical approach to decision-making

There is a way of understanding time, different from our usual linear concept, that can help us move more trustfully with the circularity of our feminine, cyclical lives. The Ancient Greeks called it kairos. Kairos time is all about waiting for the right moment, the point of readiness, the conditions that are most opportune for what is needed to happen. It is the timing of things coming to fruition naturally. Kairos time, it has been suggested, is the feminine complement to the masculine concept of linear, or Chronos time.[36]

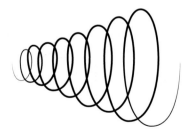

---

36   Penelope Shuttle and Peter Redgrove, *Alchemy for Women*, Rider, London, 1995. P31

Kairos time has a special resonance with our cyclical experience of life, and offers us a more womanly way of processing issues, making decisions, and taking our steps in life. When we move in kairos time everything can be taken into account along the way, as we are less preoccupied with the pressure of 'moving forward'. Perhaps we could consider kairos as *timing* rather than *time*. While Chronos time is progressive from past to future, kairos moves forward and backward, inward and outward, in the circling patterns of ripples on a pond. In its holographic way the femenome marries the circular and the progressive forms together, creating the spiral form of our menstrual cycle moving us forward while taking us round and round in ever-returning, yet ever-renewing time.

> The femenome marries together the circular and progressive forms of time moving us forward while taking us round and round in the self-expanding spirals of our menstrual cycles

Thus we are provided with a constantly varying repertoire of energies to draw from, ensuring that there will always be a kairos moment, a right-timing in our month for every kind of action, decision or response that we need to make. A woman living according to kairos time arranges her tasks, creative projects and relationships in accordance with her menstrual cycle energies, so that each is undertaken at the most favourable time in her month. Kairos time will always give us the opportunity to revisit and revise from an ever-widening perspective as we traverse its self-expanding spirals.

It is so very important for us to know we can avail ourselves of kairos time when we have important decisions to make. As with everything in conscious menstruality, we can take this to very profound and sophisticated levels, and things are not always as they seem at face value – but let's begin with a simple example.

~◈~

A woman I will call Jenny who came to me for help with her relationship was attending therapy on a fortnightly basis, which happened to coincide with the ovulational and menstrual points of her cycle. We both quickly noticed the dramatic swings that occurred and recurred according to where in her menstruality she was at each appointment. At the ovulational sessions she described the relationship in glowing terms – indeed, as irresistible. *I know it's not good, but we make love so divinely that it's all worth it. I'm sure that if I can manage to stop being so emotional, just settle for that and not demand other things, it will work. I can't give it up.* But two weeks later, as her pre-menstrual and menstrual sensitivities ramped up, she would storm in almost shouting *that relationship has to go. I can't be myself with him,* and launch into tirades of outrage and heartbreak over his diabolical behaviours and manifest unsuitability for her.

Many of us will know this story, in a thousand variations, from our own lives. Was Jenny schizophrenic? Bi-polar? Deranged? Seriously confused? No, Jenny was female, living in a cyclical swing that was sharply amplified by her hormones, because in fact the relationship *was* unsafe and very destructive for her. Although I was deeply concerned for her as she went through its dangerous and dramatic ups and downs, I also knew that if she ended it because she thought she should, or worse, because she thought *I* thought she should, that would be a decision made only from her mental faculty. It would not stick, and she would soon end up back in the same trap with this man or another.

In order for Jenny to come to a place of real, sustainable choice, she needed the fenomenal courage to allow herself to be instructed by *all* of her cycle viewpoints, even though they seemed totally at odds with each other. So, around and around her cycle-circle we went for some time, learning and clarifying a little more each month from the differing perspectives she encountered.

What Jenny discovered, and what is crucial for us all to know, is that kairos time decision-making is not about trusting certain cycle phases and distrusting others. Like so many women, Jenny believed she should never allow herself to trust a decision made while pre-menstrual. But if we rely only on our rational faculties, and always make our decisions from those, we are missing out on the vital depth-perspectives of our emotions and soul. Kairos time decision-making is challenging, and sometimes complex – because it asks us to synthesise the whole kaleidoscope of factors our different cycle-moments will throw into the mix, without favouring or trusting some over others. All are valid. All are equally important. Fenomenal wisdom lies in knowing how to combine and weave them, little by little, learning by learning, into decisions that are absolutely right for us – steps that make our soul applaud inside us.

For Jenny, as this work evolved, the real learning was not about a yes/no decision in the relationship. At the much deeper, more sophisticated and significant level the femenome likes to take us to, it was all about her need to take *ownership* of her wild sexual energy at ovulation so that she could fully enjoy it for itself without it continually pulling her back into unsafe entanglements with men who could not honour her as she deserved. In the fullness of kairos time she was eventually quite easily able to take the necessary step of ending that relationship, because she knew that to do so was not to give up on her delicious sexuality, but in fact to experience it more fully without the terrible compromises she had been making to have it in her life. Once she had *all* the pieces of the puzzle, the picture was clear, and easy to put into action.

a pause to consider…
A kairos time approach to decision-making

What are the important matters you are currently considering in your life? Decisions to be made? Issues to respond to? Actions you are needing to take? Paths to choose from? Steps to be put in place?

Choose one to work with first, as you get to know this method.

Make yourself a mendala – a big one with plenty of space in it. Or set up some pages of your journal so that you can revisit them and add more each month for several cycles.

Beginning at whatever point of your cycle you are in at the moment, record as much as you can of your feelings, thoughts, preferences, understandings, priorities, inclinations, inspirations, dreams, hopes and deep desires about your issue or decision. It's important not to do this from your head, so rather than trying to complete it in one sitting, keep your journal or mendala handy so you can add notes or drawings as they occur to you throughout all the days and nights of each cycle phase. The ones that pop up at random moments when you aren't even thinking about your issue are the most valuable, so ensure you make it easy for yourself to capture them.

It's most important that you allow yourself the freedom to write and draw whatever feels true at any point of your month, without editing, judging, comparing, or adjusting your entries to fit with what you wrote the week before or how you might feel the week after. Do not be concerned if your entries feel contradictory – that's quite ok, just different colours in the kaleidoscope. Don't be concerned with how it's all going to fit together, or what the outcome might be. Our mind is very tricky sometimes, so be on the lookout for it trying to influence the outcome by leaving out things it is scared of or adding in things it thinks should be there. Honesty is the key for this method. As you can see in Jenny's story above, the real issue is usually not the one at the surface, but something deeper that our personal femenome teacher is trying to bring to our attention. So use your fenomenal courage to stay curious, brave and as open as you can through each week of your cycle, letting each voice speak freely and honestly.

Keep this process going for several months if possible, or at least two, so you can see everything that needs to be taken into account and every part of you who wants to be included in the decision that gets created in kairos time from consulting all four wisdoms inside you. You just might be amazed at what they can come up with when they all work together! Wait to see the whole picture before you craft a decision or action or step. Be open to the possibility that it will be something quite different from what you expected at the beginning of the process!

Enjoy your rich and colourful feminine kaleidoscope.
The joy of alignment
when body, mind, heart and soul
sing in perfect harmony
is well worth waiting for!

In our creative life, just as in our decision-making, we need to look beyond assumptions that some parts of our cycle are 'more creative' than others, and conversely our fears that certain times-of-the-month will be of no use, or even a hindrance, to our creative projects. Creativity, for women in particular, is kairos in its energetic flow – perhaps kairos time at its sublime best. As every one of Earth's Nature-mirrors will show us, ALL parts of our cycle are needed, and each contributes something vital to our creative potential. Our ready-and-willing mind will no doubt be eager to take responsibility and feel that it should be in sole charge of the task. But really our mind doesn't 'get' the whole process – only its own part.

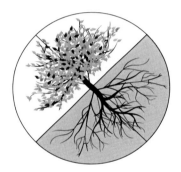

It may take some practice to become fully able to surrender into learning just what it is that each cycle phase adds to the flow. Steeped as we are in the conventional wisdom that discipline, consistent effort, perseverance and all forms of trying harder are the best and only route to the success we desire, we'll need all the fenomenal courage we can muster to help us experiment with the ir-rational and vari-able methods required for fem-enhancing and femen-honing our uniquely feminine creativity. This will ask us to accept the femenome's absolute insistence on an oscillating balance of all energies in all directions within all things; her demand that output be matched by input; productivity by receptivity; work by rest. Here is where mendala-making can really assist us to see the whole picture of feminine creativity, so that we don't panic or resist when our menstruality takes us into the seemingly non-productive phases of our creative cycle.

Let yourself remember some of your most brilliant and productive creative inspirations – the ones that surprised and delighted you, or took you off in a whole new direction you had not been able to see before. Where were you when they arrived? What were you doing? Were you leaning forward diligently into your work, fingers poised over your piano or computer keyboard, brush over canvas, concentrating hard on the task at hand? Or were you day-dreaming, night dreaming, walking on the beach, doing the dishes, staring out the window, thinking of other things entirely, or not thinking at all? Were you in the shower? Driving? Weeding your garden? Reading a seemingly unrelated book? Playing with your children? Listening to music or birdsong? Meditating? As you consider those precious inspirations, where do you feel they came from? Inside of you? Beyond you? What did you have to do (or not do) to let them in?

One way I like to envisage a creativity mendala is as a Celtic cross. It looks like a mendala[37] with a long tap root! Just like a flower on a stem, our creativity mendala needs to remind us that our manifesting faculties can only function in proportion to how connected they are to their source in our hidden inner world. In fact, if we look at our creativity mendala in relation to a plant-cycle mendala (plants are such supremely creative beings) some interesting considerations appear. Although we usually don't see a plant's roots in its visible life, we do know that they are the essential underpinning of every part of every cycle of that life – that without them everything we can see of the plant would come to an abrupt end.

> Our manifesting creativity can only function in proportion to how connected it is to its source in our inner world

---

37   The Celtic cross, with its circle echoes the ancient pagan symbol for the Earth, and all things fourfold. See p 172

And yet, how difficult it can be for us to remember it is our roots that really are the be-all and end-all of our creative life. As we noted earlier in our study of menstruation, sabbaticals have slipped out of fashion, and our unwise habits of trying to improve upon Nature instead of learning from her have resulted in an unremitting 24/7 pressure to get results; have something to show for ourselves; achieve our goals faster and maximise our outputs. This is like expecting a plant to flower year-round – it is not sustainable, it is not creative (in fact it is a painful though unintentional resistance to creativity) and of course the femenome will never allow her apprentices to be deceived by it.

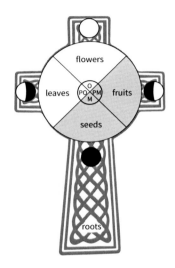

So how are we to save ourselves from the unrealistic and distressing pressure of measuring our creative success by consistent output? Let's turn again to the Celtic cross version of the Nature-mirrors all around us in the plant world: what do a plant's roots contribute to its creativity? They provide the stillness in its foundation, the unchanging element within the ever-changing cycle of the above-ground plant. They continue to draw nourishment and water from the earth, the source of its life, to send upward into the busy and active parts of the plant, long after its original seed form has grown up and left home, off into the realms of air and light to see what it can produce in the world. And even if roots down there are 'riotous' as Rumi suggests, their revelry is unseen and unheard for a whole season before kairos time brings anything from it to visible, above-ground life.

What happens for you when you arrive at the points in your creative life when, try as you might, you just can't produce anything? When nothing is flowing and the tap of inspiration seems firmly turned off? Have you noticed when in your month these are most likely to occur? If you find yourself repeatedly slipping back into familiar but fruitless attempts at discipline, or frantic searches for mental abilities that have suddenly gone missing, be assured you are not alone (believe me, you are hearing this from a world-class, fully qualified and well-practised champion at this kind of resistance, as I confessed earlier in this chapter). We know that even our computer has to be switched off before it can reboot.

the world within women

But even so, it can be so hard, so scary, to let go of forward momentum as the favoured modality, and go to what seems like the opposite extreme - the menstrual surrender that moves not forward but downward, dropping us into that deeper level of other-seeing darkness where our moonflower Self loves to bloom.

> If we can find the fenomenal trust that allows surrender
> our moonflower Nature-mirror will be there to remind
> us that the downtime has a flowering all its own

I find the femenome never lets a chance go by to teach me her ways – especially when I am most diligently trying to avoid practising what I preach! During my dedicated week of adding the final (so I thought) touches to this book I had envisaged them as small details that could easily be completed in the days I had available. I was firmly resolved to get up before 6 o'clock every morning, to make the most of my writing time at a remote beach house before returning to my busy life in the city. I went to bed full of excitement at how much I would get done the next day. Sure enough, the first birdsong woke me in the dark pre-dawn – then up I got, after indulging in what seemed just a short reverie, astounded to find it was already 8.45! I had 'lost' three precious hours of writing time – but I was laughing, because my stolen moments of staying 'a little' longer in bed had allowed my eyes to fall upon the Celtic cross hanging on the wall of my friend's guestroom that sparked this whole (new and unexpected) section for the book. I'd thought I had a pretty good plan, but the femenome was looking over my shoulder, and hers was even better. A reverie – in bed after waking, under a tree, on a sunny couch, beside a singing stream … anywhere, anytime – can be the most productive source of things our organised mind would never think of, and we should not underestimate how wondrously they can make themselves useful.

So do make plans and resolutions for your creative process, but also be willing to abandon them lightly in the necessarily unpredictable process of fem-enhancing and femen-honing the work that knows itself better than you do.

> Beyond all else it is our roots and reveries and how we allow them to nourish us that determine the success of our creative endeavours

There is no point where we can definitively say the creative cycle begins or ends. Each phase is dependent upon, and gives rise to, all others. So let's look a little more closely at the creativity mendala a plant might make for itself to see what we can learn from the experts.

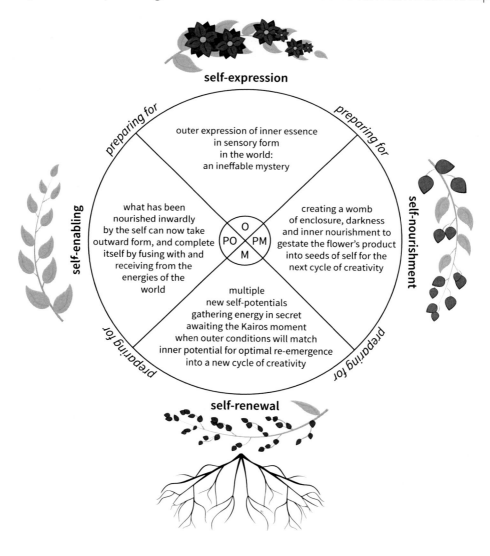

self-expression

preparing for

preparing for

outer expression of inner essence
in sensory form
in the world:
an ineffable mystery

self-enabling

what has been
nourished inwardly
by the self can now take
outward form, and complete
itself by fusing with and
receiving from the
energies of the
world

O
PO PM
M

creating a womb
of enclosure, darkness
and inner nourishment to
gestate the flower's product
into seeds of self for the
next cycle of creativity

self-nourishment

multiple
new self-potentials
gathering energy in secret
awaiting the Kairos moment
when outer conditions will match
inner potential for optimal re-emergence
into a new cycle of creativity

preparing for

preparing for

self-renewal

the world within women

The spring growth of stems and leaves (matching our pre-ovulation) is a very vigorous phase of the plant's cycle, where highly motivated energy arising from its interiorised season reaches outward to take shape in the world. At this point the plant needs to open itself to an energy other than its own. Its green leaves drink in the sky's sunlight to blend with its own creative juices of chlorophyll, stimulating a great surge of lush vitality, and the ecstatic and deeply mystical process which will become its flowering. A plant knows it must nourish and balance its own life if it is to be able to offer beauty and service to the world – and so must we. So what are the outer-world resources we can avail ourselves of, to augment our own energy and stimulate our creative progress?

Our creations, just like the miraculous flowers a plant produces, are soul portraits in physical form. I love to think of them as sacraments – "sacred-makings". Among the deeply etched rote recitations of my catholic schooling, the one I loved best has stayed with me since I first savoured its exquisite taste on my tongue in early childhood. A sacrament, I learned, is "an outward sign of inward grace". Surely, surely, I reasoned with the unerring logic of a 6 year old, flowers must be the sacraments of their plants. And so our own flowerings, our manifold forms of creative expression, are outward manifestations of *our* inward grace, our spiritual energy. They are our freely-given offerings into the world, and again just like flowers, they make it a more colourful, beauty-full, inspiring, nourishing and fragrant place. You will recognise here the equivalent of our cycle's ovulation phase. We cannot hurry our flowers, just as a plant cannot. Emerging too early they will be less than fully formed, less than they are meant to be. When we flower, all that has been taking shape inside of us, all that has been felt but not yet made, emanates of its own momentum and reveals our innermost essence.

> Our creations are soul portraits in physical form, the outward expression of our inner essence.

The third phase of the fourfold cycle is usually described as a letting-go phase. And this is certainly an energy we can learn to trust and welcome in our creativity mendala. Just as the plant begins to drop its leaves in autumn, this may be a time when we review our creations: edit, clear, prune, discard what is not working. However, this is not the only purpose of our third phase, so let's carefully take into account how a plant does its letting-go. A tree does not rake up its fallen leaves and take them to the incinerator to be burnt. It drops the spent leaves around its own feet, because even though they have fallen, they are still as valid a part of the cycle as any other. So be careful not to collapse into any negative or self-critical rampages of editing, pruning or discarding in your pre-menstrual phase. Keep what you cut, just as a tree does, to provide a nourishing compost that will feed into the renewed energy to come. And do review your reviews as your sparkling pre-ovulation mind arrives in due course to offer fresh forms that may yet redeem what was not working last month.

 It really is vital for creative women to realise that the deeper purpose of the third phase of the plant's cycle, just as with our own pre-menstruation time, is actually fruiting. And to take the pressure off this phase by reminding ourselves that fruit is not required to be a finished product – first-fruits are a good result in themselves! Neither does a plant make its fruit solely for harvesting by humans, although we might like to think it's all about us. From the plant's point of view, the fruit's purpose is to provide an incubator for its creative energy. The fruit serves as the self-nourishing womb in which the seeds of its plant's next cycle of creativity are enclosed and gestated. So let's learn from the maestros. Far from the loss of creative energy it might appear to be, this phase is an interiorising and a potentising of that precious energy, a re-charge of our battery. Be sure to welcome it as a re-seeding, not a receding!

> In the pre-menstrual phase of our mendala our
> creativity is reseeding, not receding.

The resting phase of any creativity cycle (for us, the menstrual time) is not called "down-time" for nothing. The seeds that began their life as the flower's remnant, and are then gestated within the fruit, quite literally have to go through a "down-time", dropping into the darkness of the soil below – back into the deep and original territory of roots – for a regenerative period of hidden self-containment before anything new can sprout from them.

And although it is tiny, and looks inert, the seed is in many ways the most potent stage of a plant's creativity cycle because of its fractal nature. A seed may appear to be a scarcely noticeable detail of a huge tree, and yet it miraculously contains within its miniscule form the whole immensity of that tree. And so for us. The monthly sabbatical down-times of our own creative flow are precious and necessary breathing spaces where we can let go of our absorption in the detail of what we've been working on, and connect once again in a re-visionary way with our project as a whole.

Mendala mapping your creative life

Every mendala is by nature an ever-changing experiment, a self-generating work-in-progress, a flowing energy that keeps on creating its own next chapter from the momentum of its last. So unless you have the space and materials to make really big mendalas you can add on to for a number of months, you will probably need to allow for a series to get the full benefit.

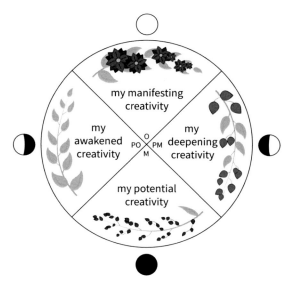

You may find it useful (and fun) to make yourself a creativity mendala based on the plant-cycle model above, or on a Nature mirror of your own choice, and matching your femenome cycle phases if you can identify them. You could perhaps first doodle up a retrospective one, seeing if you can identify what were the seed, leaf, flower and fruit phases of a past creative project you enjoyed; how they progressed, cycle after cycle, and what were the stable roots over the whole life of the work.

Then make a big mendala template (or monthly series) for a current or future creative project you want to nurture, leaving plenty of space to add more layers of reflection and discovery as you go through a few months of femenhanced and femenhoned experimentation with it. Don't be concerned if it does not appear to follow any expected pattern at first. Working with feminine energy, as you know, can never be predictable, and should not be taken at face-value – there are sure to be multiple layers of purpose in whatever your cycle does with your creativity as your month unfolds. What sometimes appears stagnant, frustrating or heart-breaking at first may not reveal its whole potential until a later part of the month, or even several cycles further down the track of the whole process.

a pause to reflect...

What was the initiating impetus of your creative project – the first seed of awareness or consciousness that let you know you had conceived a new energy inside you? The exciting idea? The inspiration? The surge of interest? The spark of curiosity? The invitation? How did you feel at this stage?

How does it want to begin sprouting leaves? Extending itself into the world to seek further nourishment? Will this be in the form of research? Experimentation? Gathering materials? Sorting out practicalities? Making notes, sketches or drafts? Conversations with others? What does this feel like for you? How does the energy originating from within you fuse with energy you are accessing from the world to become the blend that is creativity?

How does your creative project begin to flower into physical form in the world – make its unique offering seen, heard, felt, tasted or smelt? Is it appearing exactly as you had first imagined it, or has it evolved along the way? Does it surprise you? Delight you? What of your own unique essence does it express? What do you notice about your own energy at this phase? How long are you able to sustain this pace and pitch of output? Does your energy change before you are able to complete your creation? What does that feel like for you? What do you sense needs to happen at this point?

Are there phases where you realise you need to wait for fresh energy, or new inspirations before you can go any further in your creation? What do you need to do to make a growing-space available for these new ideas and motivations to arrive and develop inside you? Do you need to review, streamline, trim, simplify, reshape or relinquish any part of your work?

Are you remembering that the first-fruits of our creativity become the womb for the next-fruits to grow, and that this needs to take some inward-focussed time? Do you remember that you are the one and only tool of your trade, and that the growth of new seeds of possibility depends on how nourished and therefore nourishing your own interior life can be?

Having expended a lot of time and energy producing the first flowerings of your creative project, can you still feel the roots that originally gave rise to it? The roots of our creative works are always made of love, our own love for our project. Are you still connected to that source? Still inspired? This is so very important to check. If our love or inspiration are no longer vibrant, that indicates fatigue. We will need to remedy that by rest and nourishment, putting down the demands of outward productivity and feeding the source of our inspiration until it becomes beautiful and irresistible to us once again. If we are willing to trust the surrendering of effort, the love will return. Until it does, our project cannot thrive. Our soil may need more compost, or watering with whatever is most delicious to us. A plant will always wait for its sap to rise inside it before putting out any new leaves. What is your sap made of?

It can be very helpful to remember, especially in our inevitable creative crises, that the original impetus and ongoing motivation for our creative endeavours always was, and can only be, our love for what we are working on. Love is the generative energy, the axis around which our creativity cycle spins. So the secret of fenomenal success in our creative life is to always know our way back to that source, the original wellspring at the centre, from whichever monthly phase we are in. Let your creativity mendala-making show you the ways you can keep one finger connected to the sacramental centre at the core of your creative energy, even while the whirling kaleidoscope of your menstruality spins you through the spectrum of ups and downs, ins and outs over your month. It is this, above and beyond any other thing, that can lend a subtle yet exquisite feminine originality to all our creative arts.

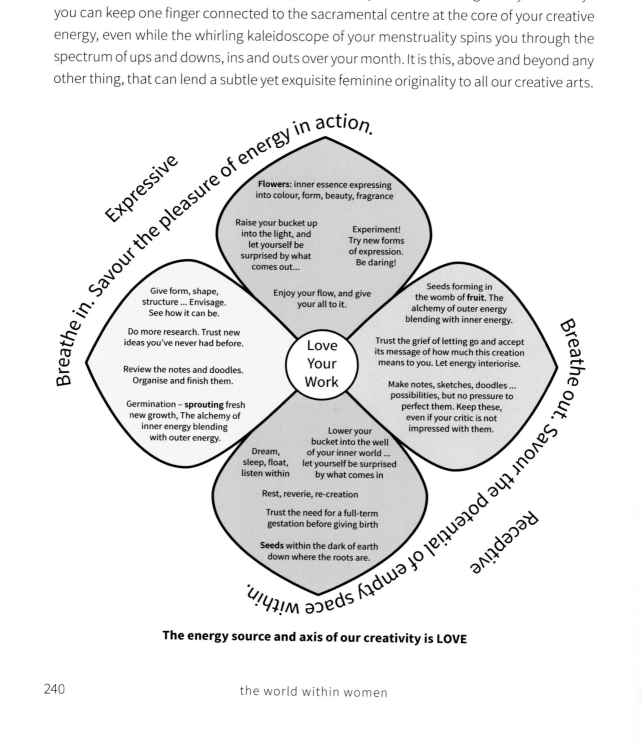

The energy source and axis of our creativity is LOVE

Our sexual mendala: cultivating a fenomenal love life

What if the whole way we have been taught to view and adapt ourselves sexually is a mere fragment, and a distorted one at that, of what is actually true about us as female sexual beings? What if the very notion of sexuality we have been sold over the last few thousand years is not something we should aspire to measure up to? Why do so many of us feel that our true sexual potential, in its *feminine* form, is never quite fully met or entirely fulfilled? How often are we left with a small and secret feeling that we have compromised, obliged someone else, relinquished what we really wanted, or settled for less? That we have accommodated ourselves to what seems available and 'normal' rather than daring to expect what we truly desire? How long ago did we learn to do this? And how many of us end up withdrawing ourselves, even at a subtle or barely conscious level, from wanting to be sexual at all, because what is expected of us is not really what we want to give? And feeling that we are not quite as we should be, or as our male partners wish we would be – that we are somehow the lower-functioning gender, sexually?

Our predicament is that, because the standards and norms of human sexuality have been confined to male definitions across most cultures for so long, we have forgotten its female counterpart may be something quite different from what is assumed. Like the gorgeous and exotic moonflower, invisible in the light of day, our particular sexual potency has gone unnoticed by eyes adjusted solely to a world we do not inhabit. So how are we to get to know what our natural sexuality is, and what it might have in store for us?

> Even though the standards and norms of human sexuality have been confined to male definitions for a very long time the original feminine sexuality is still encoded within us by the femenome

The good news is that even after such a long period of dormancy we do still have *our own* inbuilt kama sutra, *our own* divinely-sourced teachings on love-making, indelibly present and potentised by the promptings of the femenome. Like a sacred text long preserved within the secret chambers of the female psyche, this specifically feminine sexuality is waiting only for us to realise that we *can* interpret its scripts and sing its canticles as soon as we remember where to locate its keys and how to decipher its code.

Of course a full exploration of authentic female sexuality would fill many books far larger than this one. And because it already fills your own female body, your own yearning heart, your own soul-deep desires, this small chapter needs only to offer you a starting place, some femenome view-finders and some catalysing quest-ions for the joyous and liberating quest of re-embodying y*our own* sexuality on *its own* terms. Once we know what to trust, the femenome herself will show us everything that is ours to wake up to. Let your journey of sexual recovery be unhurried, unpressured and open to the unexpected. Because, contrary to popular myth, our natural sexuality is enhanced, not diminished, by our aging. You are not going to run out of time. In reality it is not until we reach the great awakening of menopause and the vast expansions of cronehood that we start to get a glimpse of just how far the femenome can take us beyond the stunted sexual consciousness of our patriarchal societies.

But what *is* sexuality? And what would *our* sexuality be if we were not constantly adapting and translating it to fit male expectations of us? We began to explore this earlier, in our study of ovulation. But let's continue to leave it an open question, for it is the living of such quest-ions that guides our own self-discovery, keeps us intrigued and allured, and unfurls the limitless answer under our feet as we go. And let's be reminded again that sexuality is something we *all* possess, and *all* express, whether or not we happen to be sexually involved with another person.

> Our sexuality is our embodiment and expression of universal or divine feminine energies in the world – simply our **being** female. It is whatever resides in us and emanates from us **because** we are female regardless of whether or how we engage sexually with others.

There is much good reason why feminine sexuality has gone into hiding over the last few thousand years. She has been grievously wounded, abused and endangered by a rampant masculinity that fears her but does not understand her[38]. And we carry this wounding, both personally and collectively. It will not be easy – and indeed it may not be possible – to fully reclaim or even re-cognise our authentic sexuality from a wounded place. So there may well be a need first of all to address any harm that others have done at any point in our life to our connection with our own sexuality.

before going further...
a pause to acknowledge

Please note: this exercise may be difficult or triggering for some women. If you have experienced sexual abuse or trauma it may be wise to do this with a therapist, or in a group with a facilitator. Consider also exploring this topic in a supportive circle of friends, or other trusted women, rather than on your own.

~◇~

Find a place that is gentle and comforting for you – a place where you know you are embraced by Mother Nature, or the mothering femenome. You may like to have around you some objects, colours, fragrances or sounds that mirror to you your sacredness

---

38   For an appalling, painful, yet helpful account of this history and its fallout in our own times you can read David Leser's brilliant book *Women, Men and the Whole Damn Thing*, Allen & Unwin, Sydney, 2019

and your feminine beauty. Ensure your body is comfortable and supported, and allow yourself to relax and sink deeply into your most intimate Self.

Feel your sexuality in its original perfection – as it was when you brought it into this world, and before it met any shocks, betrayals, wounds or denials. Allow yourself the courage to feel your natural sexuality as **it** really wants to be, even if you have never felt permission to truly live it that way. Even if you don't have words for it. Breathe into this knowing, this feeling, this allowing your true sexuality to be present, filling the space inside your body.

Acknowledge gently to your sexuality that you know we women have inherited thousands of years of prejudice that have driven her into exile. That you know there is more to her than has been allowed to be seen or safe to live in this world. And, if there is need, acknowledge also to her anything you have personally experienced in your life that has wounded you sexually in any way: attitudes, expectations, behaviours, beliefs, overt and covert messages, abuses both public and private, shaming, exploitation, intolerance, assumptions. In your original family as you were growing up. At school, church, clubs, in your neighbourhood. At work. In social settings. Sport. Within relationships. From men. From other women.

Write down everything you can recognise that hurt, damaged, alienated, restricted or in any way impacted on your sense of your own sexuality. Anything that altered your sense of okayness to fully and freely be your sexual self. To want what you really wanted sexually. To do what you preferred. To be who you really were sexually.

Then also acknowledge as truthfully as you can, in writing or drawing, the effects these experiences had on you. How might they have shaped your developing sexuality, your feelings and beliefs about being female, as a child? In adolescence? And how did they prevent you from being able to fully live, express and enjoy your true sexuality in adulthood? What influence have they had on your confidence? On your self-respect? On your sense of safety? Freedom? Worth and value? Self-love? Expectations of being able to be freely and fully your most sacred and intimate self?

You may need to take lots of time over this acknowledging, as it can go very deep and very wide. Do remember to seek support if your search becomes distressing.

Just keep gently asking within yourself if there is anything else that would like to be acknowledged, until you come to a place where every wound, every insult, every diminishment feels heard, and a calmness settles inside you.

Now, or at some later time, gather up all that you have written or drawn or collected to symbolise the harming of your sexuality. It is very important to take a deep, full breath and declare out loud or in some other definitive way that these are not you. Although these things may have shaped your life in some ways up until now, they are not who you are. They are not the truth of what your sexuality is. And they cannot be allowed to continue defining, influencing or obscuring your own view of your sexuality any longer. You need a true view now, and that can only be found by clearing off all the debris that may have accumulated around the whole issue of sexuality for you over the years.

Do allow time and supported space to grieve for what you have suffered – for all of the ways that your sexuality has been impaired or prevented from being its whole and true self. Do let this matter. Do let it be fully known to you. And if appropriate, to another or others as well.

$$-\diamondsuit-$$

When all of these experiences feel fully heard, fully known and acknowledged, decide how you would like to give them back to those people or situations they do belong to, so that you can be free to once again connect with your original sexuality as it was born in you. You may like to burn or bury what you have written – or infuse it all into a stone to drop (or hurl!) into a river or ocean. Or stand on a windy hilltop and let it all blow away from you…

$$-\diamondsuit-$$

Now it is time to begin savouring that clear space you have made within you. Let the quest begin. If those things are not and never were my sexuality, then what **is** it?

Finding our self-defining and authoritative stance on sexuality will ask us to fully understand and unreservedly accept our fundamental sexual nature *without* being influenced by the negative connotations that have become so attached to and entwined with it over the millennia of patriarchal domination. Our anatomy holds some very simple and obvious clues to our deeper sexual potentials, especially on the dark side of our monthly moon. Whereas males are anatomically full of themselves so that their sexual energy flies *outward*, we women quite literally hold open space within ourselves, so that our sexual energy draws another *in*. We are by our very nature penetrable, permeable. What is needed for us to be able to maintain this openness, this supreme vulnerability, *without* seeing it as a weakness, as we have long been persuaded to do?

> Feminine sexuality is in its very essence vulnerable. **Vulnerability is not a weakness. It takes a special kind of strength to accept and live from a state of supreme vulnerability**

The strength required to truly know, allow and *live from our vulnerability* (in itself a quality that could redeem so much in this world) is different from the male strength that we have been conditioned to view as the norm, and requires a very different Selfhood to draw from. *What is this specifically feminine strength, this Selfhood? How can we connect to it in ourselves and consciously develop it? What does it ask us to believe, unshakeably, about ourselves?* These are enormous and necessary questions that women are exploring personally, collectively and artistically in cultures all over the world, inspiring us to heal from our history.

So be on the lookout for women around you who carry their vulnerable sexuality with a powerful strength and grace; women who evoke your respect; women who fully inhabit their bodies, no matter what size or shape they may be. Women whose beauty and femininity radiates powerfully from the inside out. Because it is absolutely a pre-requisite that whatever we want others to know, accept and honour about our feminine sexuality must first be fully recognised, fully valued and fully owned inside of ourselves.

> Whatever we wish another to understand and respect of our sexuality we must first TOTALLY own, understand and respect in ourselves. What does this ask of us?

a pause to reflect...
Re-embodying our sacred sexuality

Relax and allow yourself to fully feel your body – every aspect of the feminine in you. Feel your breasts, your belly moving with your breath. Feel your heart, and all that it has meant to you to be feminine in your life.

Very gently notice if you encounter any negative attitudes/resistance/fears in yourself – any things about yourself or your femininity that you are reluctant to look at, accept or love. Write them down honestly. Ask, how did this attitude get here? Consider whether you have been conditioned to be unaccepting of yourself in any way? Do you look with a critical eye, scanning for imperfections? Be compassionate. These conditionings prevent us from being able to know or experience our own femininity accurately.

Now, take a fresh breath and see if you can open just a little more to your femininity, just as she naturally is, with genuine trust and interest:

What might I have been unconsciously rejecting/disallowing/distrusting in my sexuality?

What would I need that would help me to begin re-embodying these aspects of my Self into my conscious sexuality?

What difference would that make to how I am in my life, my relationships, the world?

What is there that I have not known, remembered, loved and claimed in my sexuality that I would like to know, remember, love and claim now?

A good way to start on your quest of getting to know your personal feminine sexuality on its own terms is (of course) by making an observational mendala of how it naturally expresses around your cycle (remembering to use the moon's cycle as a guide if you do not have menstruation or ovulation to go by). Whether or not you are in a relationship, note your sexual feelings, desires, needs, preferences, fantasies, dreams, energies, impulses and behaviours, just as they appear during your month's progression. At first this may be really simple, such as this little flower mendala:

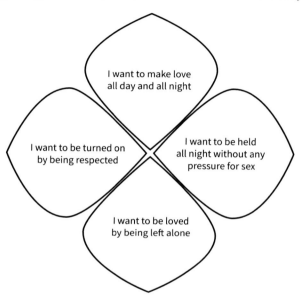

For women on hormonal contraception, sadly, your natural sexuality mendala may not be easily apparent – so stay very compassionate, listen deeply to your heart's desires, and allow your intuition free rein as you ask the femenome to speak to you through all her Nature mirrors and help you to remember your innate female sexuality.

For those who are single, give yourself full permission (and full care if this is tender for you) to claim your sexuality as freely as you can feel it inside you. Sexuality is not, of course, dependent on our being in relationship, so don't hold back from any of the exercises or reflections in this chapter. Some of us do not wish to be in relationships, but that does not mean we have no sexual self. There can be some very deep grief to acknowledge and take care of if our sexual nature has not been able to be fully expressed in our life circumstances – whether that be because we have no partner, or because we find ourselves in stale or less than fully intimate relationships. So keep a ready supply of self-love at hand if this deeply personal aspect of your life has held some sorrow.

It's interesting to notice how easily we can fall into the resistance trap of assuming that certain parts of our sexual month are "good" or "normal", while other moods or preferences are dysfunctional and problematic. This can easily happen if we're using the male model of one consistent kind of sexual energy being the standard to measure by. Of course it can seem disappointing if ovulation's lusty and sensual delights are not sustained as we become pre-menstrual. Or if we find ourselves wanting something altogether different sexually at menstruation than we had enjoyed only a couple of weeks prior. We may be tempted to lament, *why* do my sexual feelings keep changing, just when my partner and I thought we had a good thing going? And that, of course, is the perfect conscious menstruality question – *why is* women's sexuality so variable, while men's is just "normal" (for them) all the time?

The answer, as you will be well aware by now, is that feminine sexuality is as multi-faceted as everything else feminine. The femenome is taking us through a very thorough apprenticeship in *all four* aspects of our sexual nature, not just the culturally favoured one, where we are straightforwardly into 'having sex'. We are being trained to trust the *whole* spectrum of our sexual potential and to value the important elements that are not so willingly accepted, and not so often practiced, in what we have been taught is "normal" sexuality. Perhaps more than any other aspect of our femenome-ruled nature, our sexuality is all about deepening consciousness for ourselves and those with whom we share it – and if we can accept that it will purposefully change with our cycle we can start to make the most of each of the different sexual energies we possess. Our question becomes not 'what's wrong with me sexually at certain times of the month?', but 'which part of my rich sexual kaleidoscope am I currently in?'

> The femenome will invite us to become accomplished in
> *the whole spectrum* of our fourfold sexual nature

The chart that follows is a broad and generalised guide showing how your menstruality's monthly pulse is a holographic echo of the bigger dimensions of our life-cycle sexual changes, and also of the smaller dynamic within a sexual encounter, and even down to the very same shape in the orgasmic cycle within that. This is by no means intended as a prescriptive chart – the invitation is just that you take it, if you wish, as a template from which you can explore the various layers of your own sexual mendala:

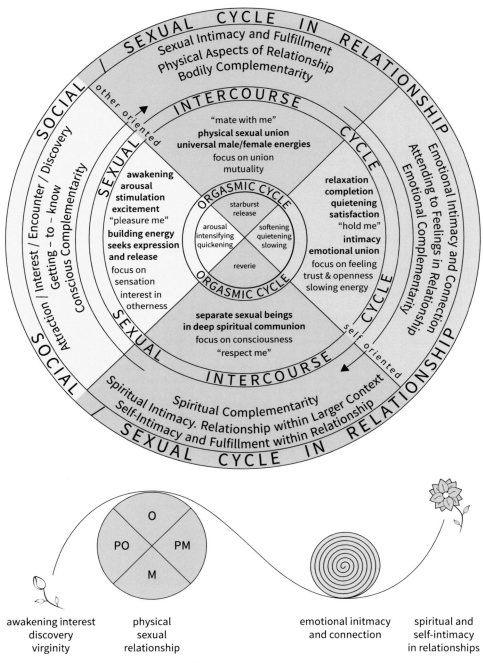

Sexuality Holograph Mendala

awakening interest
discovery
virginity

physical
sexual
relationship

emotional initmacy
and connection

spiritual and
self-intimacy
in relationships

the world within women

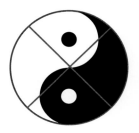

When we look at our mendala in its yin/yang form we can see how the two most commonly experienced aspects of sexuality – the mental and the physical – are its yang (or masculine) energies, while the dark, invisible and much less favoured aspects of emotional and spiritual sexuality are on the (feminine) yin side. Contrary to stories you may have heard, women are not less sexualised than men, although our sexual energy is spread over a wider spectrum than theirs, and consequently less focussed and more changeable.

As we begin delving into the femenome's dark-side-of-the-moon sexuality we will find that, just like our emblematic moonflower, who unfurls her luscious sexuality only in the secrecy of darkness, we have some very precious treasures to offer in the less-frequented sexual dimensions of our relationships – preferences and practices that can extend our range of sexual intimacy and enjoyment in some very wonderful ways. We are, after all, inviting not only ourself, not only our partner, but *our relationship*

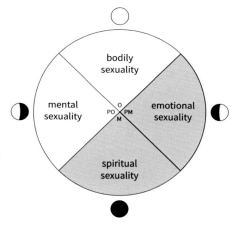

itself into those deeper, more feminine territories where so much growth and development can happen.

Do remember that the suggestions and practices mentioned in this chapter are intended only as starting points. You will find many deeper realms of your own fenomenal sexuality as you engage in your personal quest – and as you age! – and we will explore this mystical realm further in later books in this series.

Although it is not much talked about, many women experience a sharp, almost urgent peaking of sexual desire just before they begin to menstruate. This is quite different in nature from our sunny and other-oriented ovulational desire – a darker energy, much more focussed on our own need for release. A partner who understands this very particular and specific menstruality moment, and is willing to assist in a way that works well for you, can be very helpful (to both of you). Some women report that sex and especially orgasm at this peak can start their bleeding, and bring a delicious relief from the accumulated tensions of their pre-menstrual state – another kind of flowering, with its very own surprise Nature-mirror! Right here, like a sweet syncopation[39] in the dominant rhythm of our sexuality mendala, we again come upon our moonflower with her wanton petals and flagrant fragrance spilling out into the darkening night air of this seemingly out-of-season blossoming of our lust. Do pay close attention to this part of your cycle as you make your sexuality mendalas, and find out what your moonflower moment is like each month.

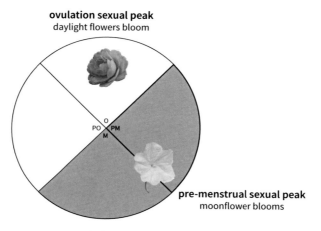

ovulation sexual peak
daylight flowers bloom

pre-menstrual sexual peak
moonflower blooms

syncopated rhythm in sexual desire mendala

and a navigational aid for the quest

Do you sometimes wish there could be more talking intimacy in the approach to sex? Have you ever longed just to be held without any pressure for intercourse? Or wanted your lover to stay awake and conscious and attuned with you in the reverie after orgasm? In her heart, every woman knows that these desires indicate that there is much more to sexual bliss and intimacy than we usually get to savour. And that our very best clues as

---

39   In music a syncopation is a surprising and enlivening alteration in an established rhythm – an off-beat, if you like, enhancing and enriching the overall effect

to what that 'more' could be are right there in the heart of our deep and familiar, but all too easily dismissed, female desires. Yes, that's right, the definitive dictionary we have to consult is in all of those impulses we have habitually discounted and buried away, because they have felt unmeetable, unobtainable, too much to ask, not what he's interested in, too emotional, too time-consuming, too demanding, too sensitive, too selfish, too spiritual, too girly for 'the real world' – or any of the other myriad reasons we have told ourselves we cannot have what we want, we cannot be who we are, and that what we have to give would not be received.

> Our guide to retrieving the full potency of original feminine sexuality lies in our deeply felt, yet all too easily dismissed, secret sexual yearnings. **They are not unrealistic – they are unrealised.** What if we dared to believe they are valid?

So an important step in finding the depth of truth we need in this quest – though it may surprise you a little at first - is to open as deeply and honestly as we can to imagining our ideal lover (unless you are so fortunate as to have a real partner who is already your highest ideal). Of course this is not about looks or bodily perfections – remember we are now in the territory of emotional and spiritual sexuality. Your ideal lover is curious about, interested in and inspired by the feminine, as embodied by you. Someone who fully sees and appreciates the most essential, authentic and whole you, just as you are – who finds everything about you infinitely precious and fascinating. Someone with whom you can easily revel in the special delights of being your quintessential self.

If this feels tricky for you at first, consider exploring with trusted women friends what their ideal lovers are like in this regard, until you feel more confident to be utterly honest with yourself. Be as courageous and gentle as you can be if doing so touches on griefs at what has never been met or fulfilled inside of you. And do be assured that allowing this imagining is in no way unfair or an infidelity if we are in a sexual relationship with a real person. It is not intended to be a fantasy that takes us away from reality. As long as we have the courage to make this about ourself, and not anyone else, imagining our ideal lover is really a way of holding up a mirror to our own unedited and unadapted sexual self, so we can get to know her as she truly is. You are not doing this to pressure your real lover to be different, but to learn about *your* fenomenal sexual nature.

The more brave and honest we can be in our gaze into the 'ideal lover' mirror, the more clearly we will be able to see what we would really desire to receive sexually, and what we would truly be capable of giving sexually, if we were being our completely uninhibited sexual Self. Moreover, it will quickly show you what you are holding back of yourself from your actual relationship, and raise important questions for you about why you do so. Does your spouse or partner even know the fenomenal sexual Self that exists in you? The more we can dare to let the ideal lover *we* can be into our awareness, the more she will become the most wondrous gift, full of potentials and invitations to offer our present and/or future beloved as we claim her.

Fenomenal sexuality – becoming more conscious

As we know so well by now, the femenome will always teach us stage by stage in her fourfold way any subject we wish to learn from her. And we have also discovered that she will not allow us to take words or concepts at face value, but will ask us to establish very consciously for ourselves what the energies actually are behind our accustomed names for things. Over the years of your apprenticeship in fenomenal sexuality you will no doubt make many mendalas – but for now here's a simple one we can explore together:

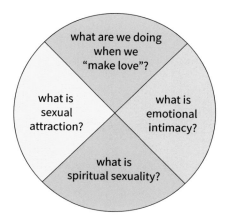

the world within women

What is sexual attraction?

We all want to be attractive – and rightly so, for it is a most important element of our sexual nature. So it is worth reflecting on what attractiveness actually is, and how we can amplify and enhance our own attractiveness by becoming conscious practitioners of this very sacred art.

Sexuality is by nature both expressive and receptive and natural feminine attractiveness plays beautifully with these polarities. By shining something of ourself *out*, we draw another *in* toward us. The more we become conscious authors of our own attractiveness, fully in charge of how we choose to use its potency, the more safely and pleasurably we can allow it in our lives.

a pause to consider...
Owning our attractiveness

Pre-ovulation is a good time to begin exploring your attractiveness, but once you're starting to get the hang of it you can try it at other times of your month as well, and see what the differences and similarities might be.

Get comfortable and relaxed in a favourite place, and breathe yourself down into your inner world. Let your memory find a time when you have felt enjoyably sexually attractive. Take some time to write/draw/dance or in any way create a detailed description of the feeling of your own attractiveness. What are its ingredients?

Now ponder these questions as honestly as you can, from the viewpoint of a perfect world where you could be **all** of whom you really are, and where **all** of your personal and unique attributes, not just your looks, are included in your attractiveness. Record your answers in your journal or on a mendala. Check out how you respond at different times of the month. And of course as your confidence with being a vibrantly attractive sexual woman increases, you will want to keep updating your data!

What about me is attractive?

What do I truly value and want another to notice and appreciate about me?

How good am I at letting these parts of myself show?

*What does it feel like when somebody **does** see and enjoy these things in me?*

What am I actually doing when I attract a person?

What am I inviting, or eliciting?

Why? What do I want myself and them to experience?

What am I doing when I turn someone on?

What of myself am I showing them?

What am I drawing them in to?

What do I want to awaken in them?

What are we doing when we 'make love'?

Sexual desire is a most powerful force – sometimes surprisingly so – and those of us not using hormonal contraceptives are most likely to feel its potent and mysterious surge inside us in the lead-up to our ovulation time. It is an urge that demands and commands our attention – a woman at one of my Luna House workshops once laughingly declared that she felt like making love even to her washing machine at that time of her month! It is also an energy of the feminine that has been feared and reviled over much of human history: at best declared unseemly and unwomanly(!), and at worst demonised and pathologised to such an extent that surgical removal of women's outer and inner sexual organs has been widely adopted as a necessary means of extinguishing it.[40]

So this is a good time for us to ask, how free do we feel to fully, eagerly and honestly explore our own sexual desire? The question 'what do women want?' has long been thrown around in a rhetorical way as something vexatious and unanswerable. Why is this so? And why have so many of us women abandoned this question, especially in sexual matters, without ever answering it *for ourselves,* let alone anyone else? I recently walked into a room where a conversation was under way between two colleagues – smart, intelligent, articulate, loving, conscious, sophisticated and beautiful married women in their forties. A conversation I (and no doubt you) have heard hundreds if not thousands of times, in all its array of variations. A conversation about how difficult/boring/unappealing (etc) it had become for them to be faced with their husbands' sexual 'needs' and desires of them, and the different strategies they employed to cope, comply with or avoid their men's approaches. How does this aspect of relationship become an unpalatable duty, and a source of concern and feelings of unhappy guilt for so many of us? Why are the only two options we seem to see for ourselves either 'going through the motions' to appease both our partners' and our own sense of what we owe them, or wanting to be left alone sexually? Neither of those is what we are made for!

I ventured a little probe into my friends' conversation: 'what would making love be if it was on *your* terms?' This produced a startled silence – and in all my years of putting that very question to women I have rarely seen a different result. It stops us in our tracks. Sadly, we have not considered what our terms would be. It seems not to have occurred to us that we could even have alternative ways of being sexual and intimate that would work perfectly well, no matter how they might differ from those of the masculine norm. Really, it is time for us to pick this long-neglected question up off the floor, dust it off, and take a good, long look at it.

---

40   This includes both surgical removal of the womb and/or ovaries, which has been believed to be a cure for all manner of supposed mental or moral disorders in women from ancient times, and the routine excision of the clitorises and labia of all girls in the 30 countries across Africa, Asia and the Middle East that still practice 'female circumcision'.

> What if 'what do women want?' is one of the most important and necessary questions of our times? What if our answers to it can really help to heal, change and enrich our world?

Once again, you will need to be generous in giving yourself time to go right back to the source in your quest for what you desire sexually. You will need to do everything it takes to find within you once again the sexual being you are, deep down beneath the layers of depleted mother, dutiful wife, or woman who has long ago relinquished any expectation of being fully met. If *we* do not know who we are, what we want, or what *we* would like to initiate sexually, how can our partners have any chance of meeting us in satisfying ways, or even knowing what is possible in fully awake fenomenal sexuality?

Whether or not we are in a sexual relationship, the magnitude of our sexual energy can be quite surprising (as long as we are not on hormonal contraceptives). No doubt the scientific rationale of 'propagation of the species' could be offered to explain our hugely heightened sexual desire at ovulation. But when we remember we are dots within the great mothering holograph of the femenome we can begin to sense the marvel of what gets so turned on inside us at these fenomenal peaks. Through our sexuality we participate in the sublime cosmic force of creativity. We are all easily familiar with the role of our sexuality in conceiving children and keeping life flowing in that way. Yet there is much more to our fertility than that. It encompasses all our creative impulses and energies – all that we love, nurture, inspire, provide and tend every day, so easily and naturally we are scarcely aware we are mothering life itself.

So why *do* we call our sexual encounters with others 'making love'? This too is a very important question, and we would do well to light it like a candle and hold it up where it cannot escape our attention. Our sexuality is sacred. It is a spiritual potency, calling us and our beloveds to open to the ecstatic realms of our being – to reconnect with the very energy of which we are made. It is not for nothing that we are irresistibly attracted to this force; that it draws us so compellingly, time and time again, to re-experience our origins in the divine ignition of life itself. It is also not for nothing that our orgasms feel like radiating starbursts of light within us, for that is what they are as we touch again and again into the

the world within women

pure source of life itself – the spark of our conception; the Love we are made of. What greater invitation could there ever be than to go with another beloved soul back to our pure and primary source – and why would we ever want to settle for doing this in a perfunctory or unconscious way?

> Our sexuality is a spiritual potency calling us back to the
> ecstatic realms from which we came, through reconnection
> with the primary energy of which we are made: Love

I most warmly urge you, if you ever come to a place where you are in any way reluctant or less than whole-hearted about sex, to take that as a wake-up call from the femenome that you are forgetting – or maybe you never realised there could be room – to bring your *whole, conscious, honest, potent, awake feminine self* to your sexual life. That you have not realised you can give her a say, or perhaps have not yet been able to find the courage that would take. If your relationship is not feeling like a place for you to enjoy being sexual it is time to attend to what is not okay for you *in the relationship* rather than deciding that your menstruality hormones or lack of sex drive are at fault.

a pause to reflect...
Re-possessing our sexual desire

Create, in any way you wish, a gorgeous temple or boudoir for the cosmic sexual energy of the femenome, and your own personal feminine sexuality within that. This could be a whole room make-over, or just a simple gesture of one object, track of music, colour, texture or fragrance that creates just the right ambience for you. Breathe yourself full of yourself, and feel within you the sexual woman you know yourself to be. Allow yourself a deep, floating reverie, in which you can open to the feeling of an intimate relationship in which your authentic innermost Self is fully expressed, fully seen and fully met. Let yourself slowly and deeply contemplate the following questions and listen for how this Self would answer them:

What is my sexual desire?

What inside me desires to be answered, and how?

What in the other do I desire to meet, and how?

What is the experience or feeling I am called to desire again and again through sexuality?

How easy is it for me to ask for what I really want (including physically) in sex?

What is it we are doing when we are 'making love'?

What is the love we are making?

What is really happening – in me? between us? – when orgasm occurs?

Do I allow myself to experience ecstasy?

If not, what stops me?

What is ecstasy?

What are our emotional needs in our sexual life?

What is the feeling you most long to feel in a lover's arms? And what most helps to create that feeling for you? If you are really honest, what is most likely to make you want to be sexual with someone? Does your partner know that this is what sparks up your love? Have you found that your answers to these questions vary, depending on what time of your month it is?

Have you had sexual encounters, or been in relationships, where physical sexual energies are the dominant factor? And have you also had encounters and relationships

the world within women

where emotional dynamics have been more powerful than physical ones? What has each of these experiences been like for you?

Have you, or other women you know, ever craved more emotional depth, or more time to find your way to emotional intimacy with your beloved, without pressure for physical sex mounting too quickly? How easy is it for you to speak your real feelings, your deep emotions and needs, without reservation, into your relationship? Into your sexual exchanges?

What if we have every right to demand more emotional content in our sexual relationships – not only because it would be very good for us, but because it would hugely benefit our lovers too (especially if they are male) and our relationships overall? Perhaps it is time to take a closer and more curious look at how our sexual energy and preferences change as we move out of our ovulational zone, and into pre-menstruation. What is the femenome's purpose in seemingly extinguishing our libido, and with it that generous and sexy self we were so happy to be in our free-and-easy week?

If we can find the fenomenal courage to trust the shift we feel as we enter the dark side of our monthly moon – and be very clear that this is not a *loss* of sexuality but a *progression* into another phase of its nature – we may well be on our way to great riches that are all too often relinquished in our physicality-obsessed sexual culture. We are not just a body that someone else has "conjugal rights" to – we are the whole woman they courted and committed to, and of course our heart, soul and consciousness are going to want to be included. We can't have a good sex life without a good love life – despite the fact that much of what we are presented with in media and other forms of persuasion tends to isolate physical sex as if it was a stand-alone entity.

> We can't have a good sex life without a good love life. Our interiorising menstruality hormones will be wanting to factor this in!

So at those times when we don't feel like having physical sexual intercourse we need to take care not to fall into negative perceptions of that, but to turn our attention instead to the femenhancing quest-ions that can open new doors of consciousness in our relationships.

What else might there be that we can tune our expectations to on the strangely neglected bandwidth of sexual possibility? Back to the stunned silence in the conversation my colleagues were having, to that question we are not yet sufficiently accustomed to pursuing in any real depth: what *do* we want instead? So often the immediate answer is 'I just want to be left alone' – but this can easily be more reactive than deeply considered. It is absolutely fine to want to be left alone, of course, but what do we want to do with that aloneness? And what do we want it to do for us? For our relationship? If sex-as-usual is not what we want at certain times of our month, what *would* truly be 'making love' *to*, and receiving love *from*, our intimate partner in such moments? What would our tender and sensitive feminine heart say of her sexuality now, if she was really free to choose?

> How might an honest sexuality mendala contribute to a more whole,
> deep, loving, intimate and rewarding sexual relationship?

Does our relationship in its current form include *on a regular basis* even a simple sharing of how we are feeling emotionally? Is our pillow talk on this level? It can be sobering to admit how easy it is for these fundamental elements of connection and intimacy to fade away as relationships become more burdened and distracted with the constant demands of life. Would you appreciate some form of commitment with your partner to checking in and catching up emotionally with each other – to listening and responding for its own sake, rather than with a problem-solving agenda – weekly, monthly, or as a nightly love-ritual as you go to bed? And if not, why not?

a pause to ponder…

Once you have explored these questions about being held (or even before that) you can substitute questions about other aspects of non-intercourse intimate sexuality, such as being deeply listened to, sharing silence, singing together, reading poetry to each other, being touched in particular ways (not intended to cajole you into intercourse!). Let your list of possibilities be truly endless!

Do I like being held by my lover?

How much do I like it?

Why do I like it – what do I receive from it?

What does it create or open inside of me? Between us?

What happens to trust? To closeness? What settles inside of me when my lover holds me without pressure for sex?

What would I like my lover to know about how this feels for me?

How do I feel toward my lover when he/she does this for me?

Do I like to hold my lover in this same way?

Why?

How to I feel toward my lover when I hold him/her?

What can go on to happen between us when there is this intimate holding?

Is there enough of this dimension in our relationship?

(but be warned – this depth of emotional intimacy can open us into a much deeper desire for sexual connection after all!!!)

Opening to the spiritual realms of sexuality

Many ancient traditions recognise the feminine as the initiator, through sexuality, into the deep realms of spirituality and the bliss of awakened consciousness. The femenome's requirement that we women traverse our interior world every month equips us in the most marvellous ways for this medial and mystical role, where we are *all*, in fact, supremely well-qualified to initiate and lead.

It is in this sacred role that the potency of women's vulnerability can best be understood. Our body, specifically because of its openness, its interior spaciousness, is the **only** passageway through which souls can *incarnate* into life in this world. Nobody gets to be here, to be human, except, via sexuality, through the mystical doorway that we are between the physical and the spiritual worlds. In the same way our openness can serve as the doorway to *excarnation* – our brief and blissful departures from, or expansions beyond, ordinary consciousness into the ecstatic and divine realms where orgasm can take us. (It is not for nothing that orgasm has sometimes been called 'the little death'.)

Since the earliest times of humanity, as we acknowledged at the beginning of our exploration of menstruality (p 21), women have been known, especially in their menstrual state, to be a threshold or opening between the worlds of matter and spirit. Between the seen and the unseen; the ordinary and the mystical; the outer and the inner realms of life. In ancient Greek times temple virgins performed the priestly rites of sexually initiating men into their interior, or spiritual life, and opening them to their own higher potential. These women were called therapeutes, and their sacred virgin service was the origin of what we know today as therapy.

Labyrinth

Another form of this initiatory service was provided by sibyls, menstruating women who guarded the entrance to the labyrinth. These days labyrinths are above-ground, able to be traversed in the light of day. But in ancient times they were a much more daunting challenge for a man seeking initiation into his own deep inner consciousness. These labyrinths were underground, cave systems running far into the dark interior of the earth itself. No one could enter without permission from the guardian sibyl, who would first assess the candidate's worthiness and readiness to undertake such an intrepid quest.

the world within women

These practices were ritualised forms of a profound but simple truth, hidden in plain sight but obvious for all to see if we are looking with a conscious menstruality gaze. The original and eternal laby-rinth is the female sexual body, whose labia surround the passageway into the dark interior that leads to…? What *is* it that we contain that is of such irresistible allure to heterosexual men? I love to ask those who attend my conscious menstruality workshops for men at Luna House (called 'light in the labyrinth') just what it is they are seeking as they come knock-knock-knocking on the heaven's door in the female body, time after time, with such high hopes of gaining her permission to enter. What is it they are so keenly hoping to find there? It is not easy to put such profound things into words, and the query always produces a strikingly potent and thoughtful silence – a good place to dwell, and perhaps a necessary prelude to the honesty and consciousness we would love to hear in their eventual answers.

> The very ethos of sexuality is to put the gifts and graces our gender bestows to the service of our loved one as well as ourself

We women are already well versed by the femenome in accessing our own interior worlds. In sexuality though, the invitation is to put the gifts and graces our gender bestows to the service of our loved one as well. So how might we become modern-day sibyls, or therapeutes, in our sexual relationships? It is highly likely that you are performing these sacred roles in many ways already in your natural femininity, so let yourself become more conscious of the innate ability you have to invite others into their inner reality, or heightened consciousness. And then consider how you might like to make this more specifically a part of your sexual life.

Ask your lovers if they know what it is they are looking for inside you when they approach you for sex. This is not a challenge, not a defensive or hostile question, and not a demand for an answer. Let it be just a loving invitation to become more deeply acquainted with the energies that come into play with our sexuality. Remember, they are divine in origin and in nature – and therefore, no matter how conscious we already are, there will always be infinitely further to go, infinitely more to be revealed.

You will, no doubt, have experienced some sublime moments in your love life where you have felt the astounding privilege of holding another soul in your arms – the sheer immensity of all that they encompass.

> The conscious awareness that we are holding another's
> divine soul in our arms is immense in itself

This can be a most tender practice to include on a regular basis, perhaps at your most spiritually open time of the month. You can enter into it just for yourself, without needing any conscious co-operation from the other – although they will almost inevitably sense it as you move into its powerfully awakening influence. Or you can invite it as an exquisite mutual practice with your partner.

a pause to experience...

Find a very comfortable position in which your body can relax completely as you hold your beloved. Breathe yourself into connection with your heart – first with her physical presence, beating steadily in your chest. Then with her immense capacity to feel the realities of life, without interference from your rationalising mind. Allow yourself some time to settle deeply into this way of being yourself.

Now let your body begin to feel in minute detail the body of your beloved, there in your arms. As you do this, let your outbreaths take you beyond all that your human mind knows of this person. Drop your consciousness down through your heart, and into your own soul, your intuitive, spiritual knowing. From there, begin to feel the divine essence of the being you hold in your arms – who they are above and beyond any human limits or complications; all of their strengths and vulnerabilities, learnings, hopes and intentions for this life they are living with you. All that you can feel of them from your own soul's perspective – all that you do know of their goodness, and all that lies beyond what you can know of it.

Breathe and feel, breathe and feel, opening yourself as deeply as you possibly can into this soul-led way of experiencing the divine presence of another so intimately. What is this like for you?

As you engage in this form of intimacy, whether it is occasional or frequent, or even only once, notice in the following days what effect it may have on your relationship.

If you and your beloved would like to do this as a mutual practice, it is probably best to do it in turn initially, so that both the holding and the being-held aspects can be experienced very fully by each of you. Once you are both very comfortable and accomplished with it, try it simultaneously for exponential effect!

Cultivating your fenomenal love life: your ever-unfolding personal sexual mendala

Once you can feel your confidence in the validity of your sexual change-ability growing strong, you may like to use the following guide to develop and deepen your personal sexuality mendala further – a big-petalled, voluptuous flower mendala might be just the thing to start on now! Be sure to avail yourself of your ideal lover if you are not in a relationship, or if doing so can take you further than you dare to go (so far) with your actual partner – remembering that this is a gentle way to help you see any aspects of yourself that you might be consciously or unconsciously hiding.

To open yourself even further to your wild and unadapted sexuality, imagine that your ideal lover sees you as a sex goddess, and has asked you to initiate him/her into intimacy with fully awakened female sexual energy. With the licensed confidence of this role, how would you arrange and conduct the sexual dimensions of your relationship at each stage of your month? What new ways of making love or being sexual might you include in your love life (and if not always focussing on intercourse, then focussing on what else?). What do you know that would deepen the love, honesty and intimacy you and your beloved could create together? What makes you want to be sexual with a partner? What would make your love life, and therefore your sex life, the most satisfying, fun, and meaningful it could possibly be?

Be generous in allowing yourself plenty of time to get acquainted with the femenome's full spectrum of sexual energies and invitations as revealed in your month-after-month mendalas. It is by no means an easy mission to begin expanding a relationship into the more subtle and less familiar realms that may not be included in the generally accepted or expected range of sexuality. You may feel you are a little out on your own, so make sure you do talk, share and explore it all in your friendships and women's circles. Our long-silenced natural sexuality may be very heartened to know that other women share her deepest and most secret longings.

And do reassure yourself – because as women we so easily get worried about the impact on others of our asking to have our own needs included – that the femenhancements we want to introduce into our sexual lives will be of enormous benefit to our partners (or future partners) as well as ourselves – yes, even if a little coaching is required at first. What we are offering, after all, is a fourfold expansion of our accustomed sexual repertoire, and quite possibly a much more whole-hearted and enthusiastic participation on our part. Truly, there is nothing in any way selfish about feminising your sexual expectations and requirements. So do be as willing as you can to be really truthful, and to let your partner know your terms. Trust that they will be wanting to know how to take your sexual pulse around the month (because it quite literally *is* a pulse-beat); what pleases you; what brings the two of you closer together, and what makes the relationship grow stronger rather than fading away with years and familiarity. Believe the secrets your true sexuality tells you. She may be a brighter and more beautiful flower than you have ever dared to believe.

My personal sexuality mendala

Imagine you are inviting your beloved (real or imaginary) into the most profound, whole, intimate and truthful relationship with you – with your deepest, truest, innermost feminine Self. That he/she has asked to be initiated into an encounter with the sacred feminine in all its mysteries, as embodied by you. Take many months (or even the rest of your life!) with an intrigued and respectful curiosity, with an open acceptance, with fearless honesty and a willingness to be surprised, to discover the colours and fragrances of the different petals of your sexuality flower at each phase of your cycle. Make a big, beautiful, ongoing mendala to explore, with words, songs, colours, poems, drawings or any other mode of soul expression, every aspect of sexuality you can possibly identify. You may like to start with simple questions, such as those below, and then delve more deeply into whatever arises for you as your own unique sexuality petals unfold, one by one.

How does the real me feel sexually at each phase?

What does the real me desire and require to receive sexually at each phase?

What do I know the real me has to offer and share sexually at each phase?

What does being woman mean to me at each phase?

How would the real me choose to make love at each phase?

How would she set up her temple or boudoir, and what would she allow and disallow in it at each phase?

How would I like/not like to be approached sexually at each phase?

How does my soul want to express herself sexually at each phase?

What are the colours and energies of my sexuality at each phase?

Make a self-portrait, or symbols, of my sexual self at each phase

Sexuality, no matter how wild or playful, is a way in which we touch the divine in ourselves, in each other, in life itself. It is the grace of which we are made. Never settle for less!

the world within women

Advancing in the college of the femenome: getting ready to graduate

The femenome has a way of forming us that is gentle, yet insistent, compelling and inexorable in its thoroughness. Like a supremely sensitive tuning fork, she minutely and repeatedly adjusts us over the years and decades of our menstruality apprenticeship until each note of our separate cycle phases is tuned to pitch-perfect harmony for the coming great chord of menopause. This is an inestimable gift to us. We carry everything forward with us as we journey through our eventful lives – that which is resolved and completed, and that which is not yet resolved and still to be completed. What we do not carry consciously comes with us unconsciously. If we have not paid attention to the ways our cycle has tried to show them to us, these raw or uncompleted energies can show up later as symptoms in our menopause. So it really does pay to take notice of what our cycle puts in front of us!

> We carry everything forward with us. What we do not carry consciously comes with us unconsciously and may manifest as symptoms in menopause. **Menstrual cycle fenomena are aids to consciousness!**

Mendala Medicine

Mendalas are in themselves sacred. They are part of the vast intelligence of life itself – a living language, a deeper heartbeat, a wiser pulse governing everything in our cosmos.

As with all mandalas and medicine wheels, their all-encompassing, symmetrical and balanced geometric form holds energetic properties that can have a calming, harmonising and integrating effect on our lives. Just having them around – working with them in any of the ways we've discovered and discussed throughout this book, or even simply keeping them in your consciousness as you go through your month – can bring subtle but powerful benefits to your health, trust and happiness.

Consider a monthly practice that can be used for healing, restoration, reflection, prayer, discernment, self-support, celebration, meditation – or just as a pleasurable activity. You can do this by yourself or magnify its potentials by sharing it with trusted friends in a circle of women. You may find that your menstrual phase is the best time for this process, offering an opportunity to reap the benefits of your completing cycle before moving on to the next. This exercise is an extension of the menstruality iridology process we learned earlier (p 216) for those who wish to go further. It is placed in this 'getting ready to graduate' section because it is intended for experienced practitioners of conscious menstruality, who have already become adept and confident at letting the femenome shape their lives, even when her ways are not easy or comfortable (an ability of inestimable benefit as we prepare to navigate through our coming menopause).

Monthly mendala medicine meditation

Make yourself a mendala, devoting some care and attention to creating it, so that you are getting a truly hands-on sense of what it holds – quite literally keeping your finger on the pulse of your own life. (If your cycle is not physically evident, mark your mendala quadrants with the four moon phases or another Nature mirror of your choice.) This needs to be a mendala on the floor, or on Mother Earth herself, in your garden, or out in the wilds. Your mendala needs to be big enough for you to stand or sit in each of its quadrants. What would you like to make it with this month? Shells? Driftwood? Flowers? Coloured beads? Feathers? Leaves? Fabric? Stones? Grasses? Pinecones?

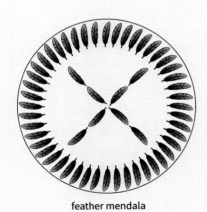

feather mendala

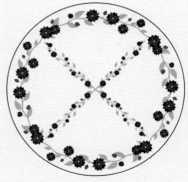

flower mendala

Step through the quadrants of your mendala, one by one, taking your time to connect with what happened at each phase for you this month, both around you and inside you. How did events and other people impact on you? What feelings were strongest at each season of your cycle? Was anything difficult or challenging during this last month? What new realisations or inspirations occurred, and when? What were the most intense days? Why? Where did you learn something new, or achieve a breakthrough of any kind? Are there any places in this month's review mendala that are still unhappy or unresolved, or proving hard to understand? Compassionately include everything you can, but especially whatever was most challenging, or most life-changing at any point during this last cycle.

When you have identified the most significant point of your last month, sit down in that place on your mendala and breathe softly until you can fully relax there. Feel the experience this mendala moment brought you, without judging it or reacting to it in any way. Notice all the feelings you have about what occurred here, just gently breathing space for them into your body.

Then, when you are ready, expand your attention until it encompasses the whole of your mendala, so that you can feel your significant moment within the context of your fourfold self. Let the other three energies around the one you are sitting in provide a holding, a balancing, supportive, integrative embrace around your intense experience. Listen very attentively to what their advice or suggestions might be, or what they can offer you and the issue at hand, as they have each contributed in the cycle just passed, and can each assist in the month to come. What would you like to request from each of them? How does it feel to know they are arrayed around you, available to you, with their different perspectives?

The most important thing in this exercise is to allow yourself the experience of **giving over** your struggle/learning/questions/intense feelings/needs/new awareness into the great mothering heartbeat of the universal femenome. In practising mendala medicine we reconnect our own personal mendala to its original source in the sacred geometry of Life Itself. And Life Itself knows everything there is to know about living. Mendala medicine offers an infusion of pure and potent feminine energy to soothe, nourish, realign and settle anything inside us that is in need of healing.

So allow yourself a long, full outbreath to gently blow away any resistance, soften your body, and surrender what you are carrying into the medicine wheel of the femenome, where everything has its place and its meaning in the all-embracing symmetry of the whole. Relax, let go, and feel yourself held in a perfection so vast that your own small struggles are less than a flicker on its surface. Feel what this is like for you. What is there to trust, now?

If you are doing this exercise alone, bring your journal into the mendala with you, so that you can write and draw the messages and realisations you receive from your femenome teacher, to refer to during the month ahead. If you are doing it as a group, sit in a circle around the floor mendala while each woman takes a turn going into it, speaking her past-month review as she steps through each quadrant, and then sitting down in the one where she wishes to focus. Once she has had sufficient time to feel her own awareness and messages (perhaps supported by a track of music, or humming or chanting by the group around her) others in the circle can gently offer their observations of how they see her situation within the context of her whole mendala medicine map, and how they see she might best avail herself of the energies that will become available to her as she traverses the next three quadrants.

You may find it helps to actually step into the opposite or any other mendala quarter, simply to find out how your question or issue looks and feels from the other side of your month, or another part of your kaleidoscope – or to do this for each other, if you are working in a group.

*And do acknowledge, even as you complete your meditation and return the materials of your mendala to Nature, you are held in the mothering forms of your interior mendala **and** the great fourfold mandala of Life Itself every moment and every day. You can rest in it, sleep in it, play in it, pray in it any time you like!*

Be freely creative with your floor mendalas – they lend themselves to all sorts of explorations and experiments. You can use dance, sound, colour, symbol, yoga, prayer, music or any form of language in mendala medicine. Remember that you are engaging a powerful and sacred energetic form, so the answers and insights you can receive for yourself or other women from this practice will be felt in your body or suggested by your intuition. Do not be dismayed if your mind remains baffled at first – it will catch up as your learning and healing are gradually integrated in the months to come.

At a glance…

Menstrual cycle curriculum
Pre-requisites for graduation to menopause level

To be ready to graduate to menopause level in the college of the femenome, the successful menstruality apprentice will have learned:

To have freed herself from cultural resistance, hostility and ignorance and to confidently read her menstruality's own language.

To have liberated herself from trying to fit into the masculine norms of cultural expectation. To totally accept that she cannot, and redesign her expectations of herself and her lifeshape accordingly

To take a psyche-logical and cycle-logical approach in all things

To be an adept practitioner of each of the four separate menstrual cycle energies, knowing herself intimately as a fourfold being

To be fully accepting of each: no favourites, no prejudice, no resisting, no disowning, no fears

To be trusting of each, so she is fully open to its wisdom and receptive to its benefits

The art of self-possession – using her menstrual cycle variations purposefully and skilfully

The art of complete self-love – willingness to look after herself as each energy phase requires

The art of being her own mother – no matter what

The art of change-ability – maintaining a gracefully variable life within constant interior change

The art of response-ability – responding, not reacting

To be a skilled practitioner of the art of the pause, at every level of the scale

How to take a kaleidoscopic, rather than a fixed view of life

The multiple and marvellous uses of mendalas

The art of living in kairos time

The supreme spiritual arts of ir-rationality

The art of balancing apparently polarised energies

The art of menstruality iridology: loving and effective self-diagnosis and remedies

The art of conscious menstruality: confidence in planning and shaping her life according to her menstruality energies, so all can be achieved with maximum ease, enjoyment and effectiveness

A kairos approach to decision-making

Fenomenal courage

Fenomenal wisdom

The arts of femenhancing and femenhoning every aspect of her life

To maximise her creativity by fully utilising its fourfold spectrum

The art of being full of herself

Supreme confidence in the fourfold arts of fenomenal sexuality

To be a consultant for herself and others in mendala medicine

Remember, none of this requires mental effort or planning on our part. Conscious Menstruality is not about having to *make* anything happen as much as about learning to *trust* and *respond to* what happens. And that, of course, is not as easy as it sounds. Yet everything we need to know, all the growth we need to grow, is already built in to our innate design. Our hormones know the whole plan. What we can now open up to, individually and collectively with all womankind, is the beautifully simple, yet radical, revolutionary, life-changing and world-transforming step of trusting the way we are made!

> Our menstrual cycle is an invitation into consciousness. Consciousness is not what we think! It is what we feel. It is who we are.

the world within women

This has been a long letter to you, dear women. There is so much to speak of, and much more yet to come, in the wondrous mysteries of who we are. I close for now with this deeply heartfelt wish for you all

May the femenome in the cosmos be a luminous guide and divine reflection to you of your own perfect fit in the sacred patterns of all life.

May the femenome within you be a lifelong and wondrous revelation of your infinite and eternal potential.

May the femenome in all women rise up singing of the bright new world we can birth together as we remember who we are.

x

and with very much love

One morning I am consciously returning to my body from my sleep state, zooming across a vast, barren expanse between one realm and the other....

In the middle of this space I pass a japonica tree, flowering profusely, radiant and luminous in its beauty. It is huge, majestic, bigger than any japonica tree I have ever seen before. Each blossom is the most gorgeous red, and the whole effect is magnificent.

I am compelled to stop, for the tree has the bearing of a teacher. I ask it, 'How do you do that?' The tree answers:

I say Yes to my own nature.

I continue my return to Earth and my waking life filled with a wild joy and gratitude. For I realise that **this** is what I need to do to bring my work to fruition. That **this** is what every woman needs to do to become herself and change the world.

Thankyou, Japonica Tree

the world within women